Target

Get back on track

Pearson Edexcel GCSE (9–1)

History

Medicine in Britain, c1250–present

Simon Davis

Pearson

Published by Pearson Education Limited, 80 Strand, London, WC2R 0RL.

www.pearsonschoolsandfecolleges.co.uk

Copies of official specifications for all Pearson qualifications may be found on the website: qualifications.pearson.com

Text and illustrations © Pearson Education Ltd 2018
Typeset and illustrated by Newgen KnowledgeWorks Pvt. Ltd. Chennai, India
Produced by Out of House Publishing

The right of Simon Davis to be identified as author of this work has been asserted by him in accordance with the Copyright, Designs and Patents Act 1988.

First published 2018

21 20 19 18
10 9 8 7 6 5 4 3 2 1

British Library Cataloguing in Publication Data
A catalogue record for this book is available from the British Library

ISBN 978 1292 24521 8

Printed in Slovakia by Neografia

Acknowledgements
The authors and publisher would like to thank the following individuals and organisations for their kind permission to reproduce copyright material.

Photographs
(Key: b-bottom; c-centre; l-left; r-right; t-top)

Alamy Stock Photo: Photo Researchers/Science History Images 11, SOTK2011 20, AKG-images 21, 25.

All other images © Pearson Education

Text
Page 11 (Source B): Horton, Charles, *Stretcher Bearer: Fighting for Life in the Trenches*, Lion Books, Oxford, 2013; **Page 20 (Source B):** Harrison, Mark, *The Medical War: British Military Medicine in the First World War*, OUP Oxford: Oxford, 2010; **Page 21 (Source B):** Macdonald, Lyn, *The Roses of No Man's Land*, Penguin Books, London, 1993.

Notes from the publisher
1. While the publishers have made every attempt to ensure that advice on the qualifications and its assessment is accurate, the official specification and associated guidance materials are the only authoritative source of information and should always be referred to for definitive guidance. Pearson examiners have not contributed to any sections in this resource relevant to examination papers for which they have responsibility.

2. Pearson has robust editorial processes, including answer and fact checks, to ensure the accuracy of the content in this publication, and every effort is made to ensure this publication is free of errors. We are, however, only human, and occasionally errors do occur. Pearson is not liable for any misunderstandings that arise as a result of errors in this publication, but it is our priority to ensure that the content is accurate. If you spot an error, please do contact us at resourcescorrections@pearson.com so we can make sure it is corrected.

Contents

① Selecting key features

This unit will help you to write short, high-mark descriptions. The skills you will build are to:

- identify different features related to a topic focus
- select relevant supporting detail
- keep your answer focused and concise.

In the exam, you will be asked to describe features of the past in question 1. This unit will prepare you to write a short descriptive response to questions like the one shown below.

Exam-style question

Describe **two** features of the work of the RAMC.

Feature 1

....

....

Feature 2

....

....

(4 marks)

The three key questions in the **skills boosts** will help you to approach a question focused on description with confidence.

 1 How do I identify a key feature?

 2 How do I select supporting detail?

 3 How do I ensure I do not include too much supporting detail?

This unit will help you to identify features and find supporting detail, and will offer advice on how to avoid unnecessary explanation.

(1) Cross out ~~cat~~ the element that is not needed in an answer for a description question.

> A sentence that identifies a specific feature.

> Some information about the feature.

> An argument about what the information suggests or proves.

(2) Supporting information can be a general description of the feature, or a specific example related to it. In the table below, tick ✓ the appropriate column to show whether each of the following details about the work of the RAMC provides a feature or specific detail.

	Feature ✓	Specific detail ✓
A RAMC medical officers staffed the chain of evacuation.		
B There were 13,063 medical officers in the RAMC by 1918.		
C The Regimental Aid Post was located within 200 m of the frontline.		
D The RAMC organised the triage of patients.		
E Members of the RAMC provided immediate first aid.		
F Each Field Ambulance Unit was designed to deal with 150 men.		

(3) In your answer, you only need to state a specific feature in the first sentence and some extra relevant detail in the second. To save time, avoid unnecessary filler sentences or phrases, which do not serve a purpose.

In each student answer below:

a Circle Ⓐ the specific feature.

b Underline Ⓐ the relevant detail.

c Cross out ~~cat~~ any unnecessary filler material.

> No man's land was difficult to work in. A detail that demonstrates this is that stretcher bearers had to cross it under shell or machine gun fire to collect casualties.

> One feature of the work of the RAMC is that the RAMC ran the aid posts. Their purpose was to provide emergency first aid.

> The Dressing Stations had few resources. From my own knowledge I know that they had enough supplies and staff to look after the wounded for a week.

Injuries and treatment on the Western Front

This unit uses the theme of injuries and treatment on the Western Front to build your skills in selecting key features. If you need to review your knowledge of this theme, work through these pages.

1 **a** Cross out the four pieces of incorrect information in the paragraph below about treatment stages.

b Now annotate the paragraph with corrections.

> The first place an injured soldier would report to was the Regimental Aid Post (RAP). The officer at the RAP could perform an immediate operation if he thought it was necessary. If the officer at the RAP could not treat the patient adequately, they would be sent straight to a Base Hospital.
>
> Once a patient reached a Dressing Station they could receive basic treatment. However, if the Dressing Station could not help, the patient would be sent to the Casualty Clearing Station, so that transport home could be arranged.
>
> Some critical injuries, such as those to the chest, could not be operated on until the patient reached the Base Hospital. This was where patients received ongoing treatment, or arrangements were made to transport patients home or back to the frontline.

2 Facts can be used to support features. What feature could you support with each of the following facts about the RAMC? The first has been done for you.

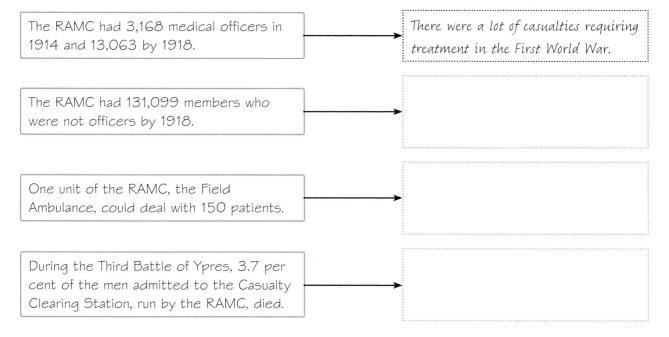

| The RAMC had 3,168 medical officers in 1914 and 13,063 by 1918. | → | There were a lot of casualties requiring treatment in the First World War. |

The RAMC had 131,099 members who were not officers by 1918. →

One unit of the RAMC, the Field Ambulance, could deal with 150 patients. →

During the Third Battle of Ypres, 3.7 per cent of the men admitted to the Casualty Clearing Station, run by the RAMC, died. →

3 Tick ✓ whether the statements below about the system of transport used for casualties during the First World War are true or false.

		true	false
a	At the start of the war, only horse-drawn ambulance wagons were used by the British.	☐	☐
b	No motor ambulances were used on the Western Front during the First World War.	☐	☐
c	Stretcher bearers would only transport casualties during the day when they could see clearly.	☐	☐
d	Wounded men were transported to Base Hospitals by train or canal.	☐	☐
e	Wounded soldiers were sent back to Britain on planes.	☐	☐

4 There were a number of developments in surgical and medical techniques in use during the First World War. Use your knowledge of these developments to work out which one led to each of the results below. 🖉 The first has been done for you.

The Carrel-Dakin method	← It reduced the number of limbs that had to be amputated.
☐	← Huge numbers of wounded soldiers were fitted with artificial limbs.
☐	← The survival rate from leg injuries rose from 20 per cent to 82 per cent.
☐	← Infections from shrapnel and bullet wounds were reduced, as it was easier to find the fragments.
☐	← Fewer soldiers died from shock during surgery.

1 How do I identify a key feature?

Question 1 in the exam asks you to 'describe **two** features'. For this, you need to identify two different features related to the topic focus in the question.

Look again at this exam-style question from page 1.

Exam-style question

Describe **two** features of the work of the RAMC.

(1) Underline Ⓐ the topic focus in the exam-style question.

(2) In this part of your course, the topics will all relate to the British sector on the Western Front, 1914–18. Some possible general features for these topics are identified in the left-hand column below. It is important to identify features that are specific. Make them specific by linking them Ⓐ to the features in the right-hand column.

general feature	specific feature
A Type of people	a Worked on the frontline
B The environment	b Medical professionals
C Use and development of technology	c Worked hard during major offensives
D The fighting	d Made the initial diagnosis
E Types of injury, disease and illness	e Organised stages of treatment
F Logistics	f Used motorised ambulance wagons
G Diagnosis and treatment	g Dealt with battlefield injuries

(3) In the table below, change Ⓐ the generic first sentences that identify a feature into specific ones. One student answer is provided to demonstrate the skill.

Generic feature	Specific feature
People worked for the RAMC.	*Medical professionals worked for the RAMC.*
The RAMC had logistics.	
The RAMC had a role in diagnosis and treatment.	

2 How do I select supporting detail?

In order to write a short, supported answer, you need to select detail that is relevant to the feature you have chosen.

Exam-style question

Describe **two** features of the work of the RAMC.

(1) A student's thought process for the selection of supporting detail for the above exam-style question is given below. Complete ✏ the blank flow chart.

Identify the feature you are exploring (see Skills Boost 1). *The RAMC worked on the frontline.*	Identify the feature you are exploring (see Skills Boost 1).

Brainstorm what you know about this topic. • *The mud on the frontline was filled with bacteria from the fertiliser used on the farmland the troops fought in.* • *The RAMC personnel were under constant threat of attack rom shell bombardments.* • *The Regimental Aid Post (RAP) was usually about 200 m from the fighting.*	Brainstorm what you know about this topic. • • •

Choose one piece of detail that either:

elaborates on the feature. *Threat of shell bombardment*	says something specific related to the feature. *Position of the RAP*

Choose one piece of detail that either:

elaborates on the feature.	says something specific related to the feature.

(2) Look at the first part of one student's answer below. It identifies **one** feature of the work of the RAMC. Annotate ✏ the answer, showing:

  (a) the specific feature it identifies – label it 'feature'

  (b) the detail it uses to support the feature – label it 'detail'.

> *The RAMC worked on the frontline. They ran the Regimental Aid Post, which was about 200 metres from the fighting.*

(3) Now write ✏ your two-sentence answer on a separate piece of paper using the ideas you noted in the flow chart in (1).

(4) Annotate ✏ your response, showing:

  (a) the specific feature it identifies – label it 'feature'

  (b) the detail it uses to support the feature – label it 'detail'.

3 How do I ensure I do not include too much supporting detail?

Your answer to a 'describe **two** features' question should only take five minutes, giving you time to spend on the other questions that are worth more marks. You therefore need to limit the amount of detail you include.

Exam-style question

Describe **two** features of the work of the RAMC.

(1) Each feature should meet the following criteria.

| State a **specific feature** related to the topic focus. | Include **one** extra sentence for each, elaborating on the feature or providing specific **detail** about it. | Describe **not explain** or link features together. |

Annotate 🖉 this student answer to the exam-style question above, to show whether or not the student has followed the criteria above.

> One feature of the work of the RAMC was that they organised the stages of treatment. The organisation arranged the chain of evacuation. At the first stage was the Regimental Aid Post, which gave immediate first aid. This was followed by the Dressing Station at the second stage and the Casualty Clearing Station at the third stage. This was a good system, because it made the best use of medical personnel and ensured that troops could be treated and returned to duty, or transported home, as quickly as possible.

(2) The answer above, if it were followed by a second feature of similar length, would get full marks. However, it would also take longer than five minutes. Tick ✓ two pieces of advice you would give to the student.

Advice	✓
Do not include explanation of the feature.	
Avoid links to other features.	
Do not include more than one piece of additional detail.	
Stop writing after five minutes.	
If you have added something specific, like a date, key term, name or statistic, do not write any more about the feature.	

(3) Based on the advice you have chosen, cross out the unnecessary material in the student answer above. This should leave you with one specific feature with one supporting detail.

(4) Re-write 🖉 the student answer on paper. Give the same specific feature but using different supporting information.

You could select from the material you previously crossed out – but remember, you only need one feature and one specific detail.

Sample response

Selecting a key feature and supporting it with the right amount of relevant detail will help you to organise your time in the exam. Analysing another student's answer will also provide you with useful practice of this.

Exam-style question

Describe **two** features of the work of the RAMC.

Feature 1

The RAMC was made up of (medical professionals.) For example, officers from the RAMC provided first aid at the Regimental Aid Posts. They were helped by stretcher bearers.

Feature 2

The RAMC's work was to treat casualties caused by the fighting. Their members staffed the Casualty Clearing Stations. This could be a difficult job, as they could be overwhelmed when a significant battle took place.

(4 marks)

Key
(Feature)
Supporting detail

---

(1) The first feature has been annotated. Circle (A) and underline (A) the second feature to annotate it in the same way.

(2) There is a little too much detail in the answer. Cross out (cat) two sentences to make the answer more concise. Make sure you do not reduce the number of marks the answer would get. Use the points in the checklist to help you. (✓)

Checklist	✓
Do not include an explanation of the feature: your answer should not say what the supporting detail means, proves or suggests.	
Avoid links to other features: your answer does not need to refer to the other feature.	
Do not include more than one piece of additional detail: state a specific feature and give a sentence of supporting information.	
Stop writing after five minutes: your answer should only be a couple of sentences long.	
If you have added something specific, like a date, key term, name or statistic, do not write any more about the feature: this will be enough to make it an effective answer.	

Your turn!

Now it's your turn to try to answer an exam-style question.

Exam-style question

Describe **two** features of the Dressing Stations on the Western Front.

(**1**) The concept map below suggests general topics you could consider when deciding on features to choose related to Dressing Stations on the Western Front. Decide on two specific features to explore, by completing 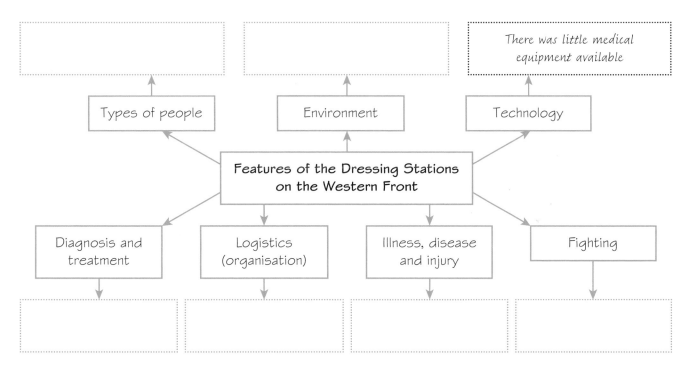 two of the empty boxes on the diagram. One specific feature has been done for you as an example, but use your own two features in your answer.

There was little medical equipment available

Types of people

Environment

Technology

Features of the Dressing Stations on the Western Front

Diagnosis and treatment

Logistics (organisation)

Illness, disease and injury

Fighting

(**2**) Follow the prompts on the writing frame below to write 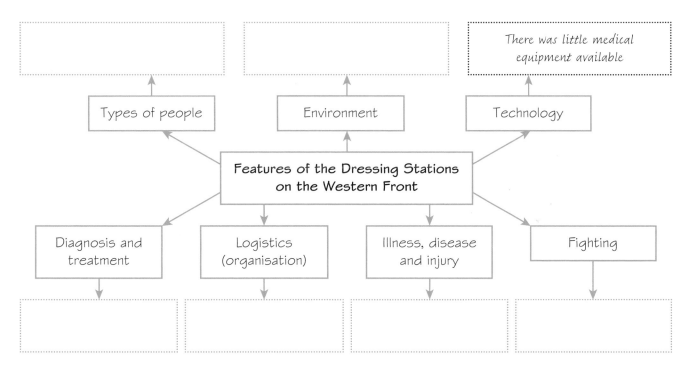 your own answer, now also including a piece of supporting detail for each feature you have chosen.

(**a**) State your first specific feature: ....

....

(**b**) Write a sentence with a supporting detail: ....

....

(**c**) State your second specific feature: ....

....

(**d**) Write a sentence with a supporting detail: ....

....

Review your skills

Check up

Review your response to the exam-style question on page 9. Tick ✓ the column to show how well
you think you have done each of the following.

	Had a go ✓	Nearly there ✓	Got it! ✓
chosen two different specific features related to the question	☐	☐	☐
selected supporting detail that elaborates on the feature or gives some specific detail	☐	☐	☐
limited supporting detail to one sentence of relevant material	☐	☐	☐

Look over all of your work in this unit. Note down ✎ three things you have learned that you will
apply when answering key features questions.

① ....

② ....

③ ....

Need more practice?

On separate paper, try ✎ the exam-style question below.

Exam-style question

Describe **two** features of the Thomas Splint.

Feature 1

....

....

Feature 2

....

....

(4 marks)

How confident do you feel about each of these **skills**? Colour in ✎ the bars.

① How do I identify a
key feature?

② How do I select
supporting detail?

③ How do I ensure
I do not include too
much supporting
detail?

② Source provenance, usefulness and reliability

This unit will help you to analyse and evaluate the usefulness of a source. The skills you will build are to:

- select criteria for source evaluation
- focus your answer on a specific enquiry
- apply your contextual knowledge to an evaluation of source utility.

In the exam, you will be asked to judge the usefulness of two sources. This unit will prepare you to write your own response to this type of question.

Exam-style question

Study Sources A and B.

How useful are Sources A and B for an enquiry into the problems faced by stretcher bearers on the Western Front?

Explain your answer, using Sources A and B and your knowledge of the historical context. **(8 marks)**

Source A *A photograph of a stretcher party carrying a wounded British soldier during the Third Battle of Ypres (Passchendaele) in August 1917.*

Source B *From an account by Charles Horton, who was an RAMC stretcher bearer at the Third Battle of Ypres (1917). He wrote his recollections in 1970.*

My squad is following behind another, some 50 yards ahead on this same road. Each party has a loaded stretcher carried shoulder-high. Then with a swish and a very loud bang a shell explodes ahead of us and the squad in front collapses to the ground.

We hurry forward and find that only one of the bearers has suffered actual injury. He has a horrible gash in the flesh of his thigh. Each of us carries what is called a 'shell-dressing' … and we use one of these and bandage it on.

The three key questions in the **skills boosts** will help you to generate ideas on how to write about source utility.

① How do I select criteria for evaluating a source?

② How do I evaluate the usefulness of a source for a specific enquiry?

③ How do I evaluate the usefulness of a source from what I already know?

(1) Knowledge of the terms used in source analysis, evaluation and judgement will help with this unit. Look at each of the definitions below, then write (✎) a summary of each. The first has been done for you.

Term	Definition	Summary
Nature	The form a source takes, such as a photograph, letter, official record or diary.	Type of source
Origin	The person who wrote or created a source, where and when they did it.	
Purpose	The reason a source was created, such as to inform, to persuade or to entertain.	
Provenance	The background details about a source, including its nature, origin and purpose (NOP).	
Usefulness	The ways in which a historian could make use of a source for a particular enquiry.	
Reliability	The extent to which a historian could trust a source to reveal the truth about the past.	
Criteria	The means by which a source's usefulness can be measured; reasons for a judgement on its utility.	

(2) It is helpful to focus on the positives of a source first, before exploring its limitations. Tick (✓) which of these statements are positive about Source A.

A | The source gives an accurate view of the problem of the terrain for stretcher bearers. | ☐

B | The source is a photograph, which may have been framed to suggest there were a lot of stretcher bearers available. | ☐

C | The source is from the Battle of Passchendaele, showing the problems faced during the middle of a battle. | ☐

D | The source suggests the terrain was difficult to walk in. | ☐

E | The source only gives us a picture of the problems on the battlefield, rather than at the other stages of the evacuation route. | ☐

Medical treatment on the frontline

This unit uses the theme of medical treatment on the frontline to build your skills in evaluating a source's utility by thinking about its provenance, reliability and context. If you need to review your knowledge of this theme, work through these pages.

1. Choose ✓ the category A–D that each of the statements in the table belongs to.

A | The system of transport on the Western Front

C | The stages of treatment areas along the Western Front

B | The problems of transport and communication on the Western Front

D | Significance for medical treatment of the nature of the terrain

		A	B	C	D
a	Stretcher bearers carried the wounded from the frontline.				
b	Soldiers fought on farmland treated with fertiliser, risking infection.				
c	The Regimental Aid Post (RAP) was within 200 m of the frontline.				
d	Stretcher bearers worked day and night to save lives.				
e	Horse-drawn ambulance wagons struggled on the muddy ground.				
f	Stretcher bearers risked their lives under shell bombardments and machine gun fire.				
g	The first motor ambulances were sent to the frontline in October 1914.				
h	The roads were destroyed by the fighting.				
i	The terrain made evacuation from the battlefield painful for the wounded.				
j	Ambulance trains slowed down the rail network for other war supplies.				
k	The RAP sent wounded or ill soldiers to the Dressing Station.				
l	The Dressing Station was staffed by a Field Ambulance unit.				

2. Write ✎ a one-sentence answer for each of the questions below.

a Why did stretcher bearers play an essential role on the Western Front?

....

b What do you think was the biggest problem for a soldier transporting the wounded off the battlefield?

....

c Why was it essential to have the RAP so close to the frontline?

....

d How do you think the terrain made the situation worse for casualties?

....

3 Tick ✓ the correct answer for each question about conditions requiring medical treatment during the First World War.

a Why could one shell injure multiple people?

A | It exploded into fragments called shrapnel. ☐

B | Soldiers had no protection from shell bombardments. ☐

C | It caused fires that were difficult to put out. ☐

b Which part of a soldier's body was most at risk from shrapnel?

A | The head and shoulders. ☐

B | The arms and legs. ☐

C | The chest. ☐

c What advantage did machine guns have over rifles?

A | They were faster. ☐

B | They were more accurate. ☐

C | They were easier to transport. ☐

d Why could a bullet wound lead to infection?

A | Germans treated the bullets with bacteria. ☐

B | Bullets could fracture bones. ☐

C | Fragments of bacteria-ridden uniform entered the body with the bullet. ☐

4 Draw 🖉 lines to match each battle with the specific fact that relates to it.

A October 1914: The First Battle of Ypres	**a** 20,000 men died on the first day of the battle.
B April 1915: The Second Battle of Ypres	**b** The British kept control of the Channel ports.
C July 1916: The Battle of the Somme	**c** The British advance cost 245,000 British casualties.
D April 1917: The Battle of Arras	**d** The first battle where tanks were used on a large scale.
E July 1917: The Third Battle of Ypres	**e** The first significant use of gas on the Western Front.
F October 1917: The Battle of Cambrai	**f** The British hid in tunnels near the German trenches.

How do I select criteria for evaluating a source?

In order to evaluate the strength of a source, you need to choose and apply criteria that are relevant to the source, such as how authoritative or typical it is.

Exam-style question

How useful are Sources A and B for an enquiry into the problems faced by stretcher bearers on the Western Front?

① **a** Before you can evaluate the strength of a source, you need to consider its provenance (**NOP**). You can use the source details to do this. Source B gives us details of its **N**ature and **O**rigin, but not its **P**urpose. Circle (A) the nature of the source and highlight the origin.

Source B *From an account by Charles Horton, who was an RAMC stretcher bearer at the Third Battle of Ypres (1917). He wrote his recollections in 1970.*

b Then tick ✓ the most appropriate purpose in the suggestions below.

To persuade the government to change their approach to the war.	☐	To recall the conditions on the Western Front.	☐
		To describe his experiences to a friend.	☐

② Consider how much you know about the source to help you choose ✓ a criterion from the options below.

If you know most about...	Choose to evaluate how...	✓
the position or experience of the author/creator.	...authoritative the source is.	
how many people's experiences the source can account for or reflect.	...typical the source is.	
the background and purpose of the source's author/creator.	...objective or reliable the source is.	

③ **a** Depending on your answer to ②, ask one of the questions below of Source B. Tick ✓ your choice.

Criteria	Question to ask of the source	✓
Authoritative	How far does the person who produced the source have the knowledge, or experience, to tell us about the enquiry?	
Typicality	How far does the nature of the source allow us to get a representative view of the enquiry topic?	
Objectivity	How far does the perspective and purpose of the author/creator of the source affect the view it gives on the enquiry topic?	
Reliability	How far can the author/creator of the source be trusted to tell us about the enquiry?	

b Now answer your chosen question.

....

....

....

2 How do I evaluate the usefulness of a source for a specific enquiry?

When you look for useful contents in a source, you must consider the topic focus of the enquiry. Then you can think about what strengthens or weakens the usefulness of that content.

Exam-style question

How useful are Sources A and B for an enquiry into the problems faced by stretcher bearers on the Western Front?

1. Underline (A) the topic focus in the exam-style question.

2. Pick out three pieces of information from Source B (on page 11) and write (✏) them into the boxes below. One has been provided for you.

> Horton carried a loaded stretcher.

⬜

⬜

⬜

3. Tick (✓) one piece of information from (2) that is related directly to the topic focus. Then make an inference about the topic focus from your choice. (✏)

Shows focus on the question	Source B is useful as it tells us about ....
Introduces a relevant detail from the source (information)	because it says/shows ....
Makes an inference from the detail, suggesting what it can tell us about the topic focus of the enquiry	This is useful because it suggests ....

4. Next, you need to consider what you know that strengthens or weakens the usefulness of the contents of the source. Pick (✓) one piece of contextual knowledge that suggests your inference is accurate.

> There were 245,000 casualties at the Third Battle of Ypres. ⬜

> The terrain was very muddy during the Third Battle of Ypres due to poor weather conditions. ⬜

> Stretcher bearers would carry the wounded from the battlefield at both day and night time. ⬜

5. Continue your answer to (3), using your choice in (4) to strengthen the usefulness of the content you picked out from Source B. (✏)

> This is an accurate suggestion, because I know that ....
> ....
> ....
> ....

3 How do I evaluate the usefulness of a source from what I already know?

In the process of applying criteria to reach a judgement on the utility of a source, you also need to use your contextual knowledge to consider its provenance.

Exam-style question

How useful are Sources A and B for an enquiry into the problems faced by stretcher bearers on the Western Front?

(1) Write ✎ the provenance of Source B into the table.

Nature	
Origin	
Purpose (if clear)	

(2) Use the prompts on the spider diagram below to identify some contextual knowledge relevant to the provenance of Source B. Write ✎ your knowledge underneath the diagram.

B What do you know about the person, or type of person, who produced the source?

A How was this type of source produced?

Contextual knowledge to evaluate a source

C What do you know about the place and time that the source relates to?

E Why do you think this source was produced? (its likely purpose)

D What do you know about the place and time the source was produced? (if different from C)

....

....

....

....

(3) You can use your contextual knowledge to help evaluate the usefulness of a source.

	B	...then you can use it in an evaluation of how...	authoritative the source is.
If you know...	B or C		typical the source is.
	B, D or E		objective the source is.
	any of them		reliable the source is.

For example, use your knowledge about B to explain why Source B is useful to a historian enquiring into the problems faced by stretcher bearers on the Western Front. ✎

....

....

....

Sample response

A strong answer to a usefulness question will focus on a specific enquiry and use criteria, supported by contextual knowledge, to evaluate a source. The student answer below does some of these things.

Exam-style question

How useful are Sources A and B for an enquiry into the problems faced by stretcher bearers on the Western Front?

A Contextual knowledge used to support a claim about a strength of the source for the enquiry.

B Contextual knowledge used to support a claim about a weakness of the source for the enquiry.

C Contextual knowledge used to judge typicality.

D Evaluation of the strengths of the source (how authoritative, typical, objective or reliable it is).

E Evaluation of the weakness of the source.

F Link to the topic focus of the enquiry.

> Source B is useful for an enquiry about the problems faced by stretcher bearers, because it describes the wound caused by a shell. The stretcher bearer in the source had a shell dressing, which suggests that this was a problem that stretcher bearers had to deal with often. This is accurate, as shelling and shrapnel accounted for 58% of the wounds in the First World War.
>
> Source B's usefulness is strengthened by the fact it comes from a RAMC stretcher bearer. More authority can be given to the problems described in this source, because the RAMC organised the chain of evacuation. This included the difficult transfer from the Regimental Aid Post to the Dressing Station, like the one Horton had to do under fire. But this may not be typical as it is only one man's experience.

1. The features listed around the student answer relate to the last skills boost. Annotate ✏️ the answer to show which of these features the student has used in the answer.

2. Which of the features in 1 did the student not use? List them below and suggest how the student could have addressed them in their answer. ✏️

....

....

....

....

....

....

....

....

....

Your turn!

Now it's your turn to try to answer an exam-style question.

Exam-style question

How useful are Sources A and B for an enquiry into the problems faced by stretcher bearers on the Western Front?

1) This chapter has focused on Source B so far. Use the table below to plan 🖉 a response for Source A.

What is the topic focus of the enquiry?		Look at the words after 'enquiry' in the exam-style question.
What can you learn from the content of the source?		Pick out content that relates to the topic focus.
What do you know that supports or challenges the accuracy of the contents?		Use own knowledge that links directly to the content you chose.
What does the source caption tell you about its provenance?		What is its NOP?
What do you know about the provenance from your contextual knowledge?		What do you know about this type of source, person, place or time?
How does this affect the strength of the source for the enquiry (refer to criteria)?		Criteria include how authoritative, typical, objective or reliable the source is.

2) Write up 🖉 your paragraph about Source A using the table plan to structure your response.

....

....

....

....

....

....

....

Review your skills

Check up

Review your response to the exam-style question on page 19. Tick ✓ the column to show how well you think you have done each of the following.

	Had a go ✓	Nearly there ✓	Got it! ✓
selected criteria to evaluate the strengths and weaknesses of the source	☐	☐	☐
focused my analysis and evaluation on the enquiry topic	☐	☐	☐
used my contextual knowledge to evaluate the usefulness of the source	☐	☐	☐

Look over all of your work in this unit. Note down ✎ on a separate piece of paper three things you have learned that you will apply when evaluating the usefulness of a source.

Need more practice?

On separate paper, try ✎ the exam-style question below.

Exam-style question

Study Sources A and B below.

How useful are Sources A and B for an enquiry into the medical treatment available on the frontline? Explain your answer, using Sources A and B and your knowledge of the historical context. **(8 marks)**

Source A A medical officer providing treatment on the frontline, from a 1917 edition of The War Illustrated, *a British war magazine.*

Source B Diary entry of Private Frank Ridsdale, 1 July 1916. He worked at the Regimental Aid Post during the Battle of the Somme.

First wounded arrive at 8am. We are very busy, as wounded are coming in by the hundreds. The road to the hospital is like the way to a football match. It is a pathetic sight, as the men are lined up 4 deep to be dressed.

At midnight I am asked to dress wounds straight away. I have been working all night, dealing with terrible wounds. Doing dressings in a dug out by the aid of a candle. I am very tired, There has been one death in the night and the men moaned in agony. A terrible bombardment overnight shook the place, making it a never to be forgotten night.

How confident do you feel about each of these **skills**? Colour in ✎ the bars.

1 How do I select criteria for evaluating a source?
☐☐☐☐

2 How do I evaluate the usefulness of a source for a specific enquiry?
☐☐☐☐

3 How do I evaluate the usefulness of a source from what I already know?
☐☐☐☐

③ Source enquiry

This unit will develop your ability to follow up a source. The skills you will build are to:

- select detail from a source that is relevant to the topic in the question
- frame a source enquiry question that relates to both the source and the topic in the question
- choose a type of source that supports your planned enquiry question.

In the exam, you will be asked to plan an enquiry based on one source. This unit will prepare you to write your own response to this type of question.

Exam-style question

Study Source A.

How could you follow up Source A to find out more about the effectiveness of the system of transport for the wounded?

In your answer, you must give the question you would ask and the type of source you could use.

Source A

An official British photograph of first aid treatment at an advanced Dressing Station on the Western Front. It was taken during the Battle of the Somme and published in 1916.

Exam-style question

Study Source B.

How could you follow up Source B to find out more about the problems of ill health arising from the trench environment?

In your answer, you must give the question you would ask and the type of source you could use.

Source B

From the memories of Kathleen Yarwood, who worked as a nurse at the Dearnley Military Hospital in Rochdale in England. She described her experiences for a book published in 1980.

Some of the trench-feet and frostbite cases were so bad that they had to be sent back to England for treatment. We had a tremendous number of frostbite cases at the beginning of 1917. In fact we had a whole ward of them … We had to rub their feet every morning and every evening with warm olive oil … massage it well in and wrap their feet in cotton wool and oiled silk – all sorts of things to keep them warm … Their feet were absolutely white, swollen up and dead. Some of their toes dropped off with it, and their feet looked dreadful.

The three key questions in the **skills boosts** will help you to develop strategies to follow up a source quickly and effectively.

> ① **How do I decide on a source enquiry?**

> ② **How do I plan a source enquiry?**

> ③ **How can I ensure my source supports the question?**

(1) In the exam, you will be expected to refer to specific sources, like 'the diary of a medical officer at a Regimental Aid Post', rather than generic ones, like 'a diary'. Use the spider diagram below to re-write each of the generic sources in the table as specific ones. One has been done for you.

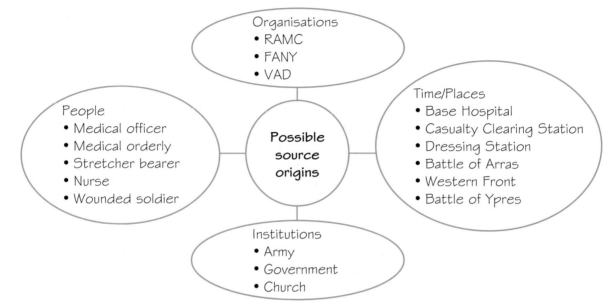

Generic type of source	Specific type of source
Diary	Diary of a medical officer at a Dressing Station
Records	
Statistics	
Orders	
Newspaper	
Accounts	

(2) The different types of sources, identified in (1), can help in different ways. Match up the type of source to the way it could help a historian.

A Diary	a It can give an idea of how common something was.
B Statistics	b It can give a view of one person's experience of a situation.
C Order	c It can reveal what was supposed to have happened.
D Newspaper	d It can help to reconstruct the supplies, equipment and people who worked in a particular place.
E Accounts	e It can give a national, or regional, view of an individual, event or development.

The trenches, transport and treatment on the Western Front

This unit uses the theme of the trenches, transport and treatment on the Western Front to build your skills in source enquiry. If you need to review your knowledge of this theme, work through these pages.

1 Match up 🖉 the detail about the terrain to its significance for medical treatment.

Detail	Significance
A It was very wet and muddy.	**a** It increased the risk that cuts would lead to diseases like tetanus.
B The ground was full of craters.	**b** Casualties could suffer severe blood loss before being treated.
C The soil was treated with fertiliser.	**c** Feet were wet for much of the time, causing trench foot.
D There was some distance between the frontline and the Dressing Station.	**d** It increased the risk of infection from bacteria in the soil.
E Both sides used barbed wire.	**e** It made it more difficult to transport the wounded.

2 Tick ✓ whether each of the details in the table relate to trench foot, trench fever or shell shock.

	Trench foot ✓	Trench fever ✓	Shell shock ✓
A It had flu-like symptoms.			
B Whale oil was rubbed into feet to protect them.			
C It was caused by the psychological strain of trench warfare.			
D It was caused by standing in cold, wet mud.			
E It was carried by lice.			
F It could lead to a complete mental breakdown.			

3 Answer the multiple-choice questions about the system of transport used for casualties on the Western Front. Tick ✓ the correct answer to each.

a Why were horse-drawn ambulance wagons not ideal for wounded soldiers?

A | Horses were not used to warfare ☐

B | The wagons shook casualties about ☐

C | It was difficult to look after the horses ☐

b How many additional motorised ambulance wagons had been bought by October 1914?

A | 51 ☐

B | 512 ☐

C | 5,120 ☐

(4) Answer ✓ the multiple-choice questions about the system of transport used for casualties on the Western Front.

    a Why were horse-drawn ambulances still used after the introduction of motorised ones?

        A   Motor vehicles could not move on really muddy terrain   ☐

        B   Soldiers did not trust motor ambulances   ☐

        C   There were only a few available   ☐

    b Which of the following was **not** a feature of an ambulance train?

        A   Spaces for stretchers in the carriages   ☐

        B   Operating theatre carriages   ☐

        C   Railway lines going up to the frontline trenches   ☐

    c Why was less use made of trains for transporting casualties later in the war?

        A   They used too much fuel   ☐

        B   They kept breaking down   ☐

        C   They delayed the movement of troops and supplies   ☐

(5) Number ✐ the stages of treatment areas in the correct order.

Returned to Britain ☐	Dressing Station ☐	Regimental Aid Post ☐
Base Hospital ☐	Casualty Clearing Station ☐	

(6) Complete ✐ the text, using words from your own knowledge, about the role of Dressing Stations on the Western Front.

One important stage of the .... of evacuation was the Dressing Station. The wounded and ill were sent there by the .... officers at their Regimental Aid Post. The closest to the .... line was called the Advanced Dressing Station, which was followed by the Main Dressing Station about half a mile further away. The accommodation at both types of Dressing Station was ...., usually tents or abandoned buildings.

The Dressing Stations were staffed by medical officers, medical orderlies and .... bearers. Collectively, they were known as the Field .... Unit, which could look after about 150 wounded men for a week or so. The wounded men reached the Dressing Stations by .... there, or were transported on stretchers. Once they arrived, they received some treatment and were transported on to a Casualty .... Station or back to the frontline.

1 How do I decide on a source enquiry?

In a source enquiry, you need to choose a detail from the source that relates to the topic in the question and can be investigated further.

Exam-style question

Study Source A.

How could you follow up Source A to find out more about the effectiveness of the system of transport for the wounded?

① The detail you choose must focus on the topic in the question. Highlight 🖉 the topic in the exam-style question.

② Annotate 🖉 the source, labelling any details that relate to the topic in the exam-style question.

Source A *An official British photograph of first aid treatment at an advanced Dressing Station on the Western Front. It was taken during the Battle of the Somme and published in 1916.*

③ Circle Ⓐ any of your annotated details that you think could be investigated further. Consider the questions below to help you decide which to circle. If you can answer 'yes', you could choose that detail to investigate.

> **?** Could your chosen detail lead to an enquiry about the topic?

> **?** Would anyone else have written, photographed or filmed about this detail/a similar detail?

④ **a** Write 🖉 your chosen detail in the table below and explain how it relates to the topic.

Chosen detail	How it relates to the topic

b Give an example 🖉 of another type of person (e.g. journalist, photographer, medical officer) or institution (e.g. government, army, hospital) that might have produced a source about this.

② How do I plan a source enquiry?

In order to plan a source enquiry, you need to frame a question that relates to your chosen detail and the topic stated in the question.

Exam-style question

Study Source A.

How could you follow up Source A to find out more about the effectiveness of the system of transport for the wounded?

① **a** Highlight 🖉 the topic in the exam-style question.

b One detail from the list below has been ticked as relating to the topic focus in the question. Tick ✓ another detail from the list below that relates to the topic and which you want to follow up.

Detail	✓
Four men are treating a wounded patient.	
There are two motor ambulances.	✓
The motor ambulances have covered wagons.	
Patients are kept on stretchers.	
A shell bombardment is going on in the distance.	

② Write 🖉 your chosen detail in the table below. Frame 🖉 a question about your detail, using one of the ideas below or your own. An example is provided.

How common or typical something was.	Why something was a problem or issue.	How a detail in the source came about.

What the consequences of something were.	The wording of the exam-style question itself.

Detail in Source A that I would follow up	Question I would ask
Patients are kept on stretchers.	Why were some people left to wait on stretchers during their transportation?

③ Check ✓ that your question meets the criteria below and alter it if necessary.

Checklist	✓
It relates directly to your chosen detail.	
It is about an aspect of the topic in the exam-style question.	
A historian could find out the answer.	

④ Follow the same process using the same source, but for an enquiry about the effectiveness of Dressing Stations in dealing with casualties. Write 🖉 your chosen detail and question on paper.

3 **How can I ensure my source supports the question?**

In the process of source selection, you need to choose one that could answer your planned question, revealing something about your chosen detail.

Exam-style question

Study Source A.

How could you follow up Source A to find out more about the effectiveness of the system of transport for the wounded?

1 A student has chosen a detail and framed their enquiry question for the exam-style question above.

Detail in Source A that I would follow up:	Question I would ask:
Patients are kept on stretchers while they wait.	How long did patients have to wait on stretchers at Dressing Stations?

Write 🖊 three possible sources the student could use to help answer their question. One idea is included below, but there are more on page 22.

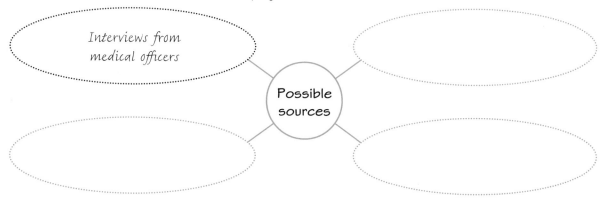

Interviews from medical officers

Possible sources

2 Highlight 🖊 one of your source ideas that could help in one or more of the ways in the checklist below.

Checklist	✓
The source provides more details, rather than repeating those in the supplied source.	✓
It places the chosen detail into a wider context, giving the bigger picture.	✓
It confirms that the detail you have selected gives an accurate impression of the situation.	✓

3 Look at this student answer, which uses one of the reasons above to say how the source might help answer the question. Try 🖊 the same thing with the source you highlighted.

What type of source I could use:	Interviews from medical officers.
How this might help answer my question:	It could place the detail into the wider context of waiting times in a battle against day-to-day operations.
What type of source I could use:	
How this might help answer my question:	

Sample response

Now you have developed your ability to plan an enquiry and select an appropriate source for it, have a go at assessing a sample student answer.

Exam-style question

Study Source B on page 21.

How could you follow up Source B to find out more about the problems of ill health arising from the trench environment?

In your answer, you must give the question you would ask and the type of source you could use.

Complete the table below. (4 marks)

Detail in Source B that I would follow up:

'We had a tremendous number of frostbite cases'

Question I would ask:

How many people suffered from trench foot?

What type of source I could use:

Hospital records

How this might help answer my question:

It would say how many people suffered from trench foot.

1. Study the student answer above, then tick ✓ the one thing the student has done correctly.

Checklist	✓
Has the student chosen a detail that relates to the topic in the exam-style question?	
Has the student framed a question that relates to the detail and the topic?	
Has the student chosen a specific source that could help answer their question?	

2. Choose ✓ a valid question that the student could have used instead for their chosen detail.

How effective was the olive oil treatment? ☐   How often did toes drop off? ☐

How many people suffered from frostbite? ☐

3. Make the source the student has chosen more specific. ✎   You could add after 'Hospital records' the words 'from', 'made by' or 'of'.

Hospital records ....

Your turn!

Now it's your turn to try to answer an exam-style question.

Exam-style question

Study Source B on page 21.

How could you follow up Source B to find out more about the problems of ill health arising from the trench environment?

In your answer, you must give the question you would ask and the type of source you could use.

Complete the table below. **(4 marks)**

Detail in Source B that I would follow up:

....

Question I would ask:

....

What type of source I could use:

....

How this might help answer my question:

....

(1) Before you write up your answer in the exam-style question, follow 🖉 the steps in the planning table below to ensure you write a strong response.

Planning table	
1 What is the topic in the question?	
2 List two to three details in the source that relate to the topic.	
3 Highlight one detail that could lead to an enquiry about the topic and which there are likely to be other sources about.	
4 Frame a question that relates to your selected detail, is about an aspect of the topic in the exam-style question and that a historian could answer.	
5 Choose a specific type of source that could provide more details to answer your planned question, place your selected detail in context or could confirm the accuracy of the supplied source.	
6 Tick which of these your chosen type of source helps with.	It provides more details to answer your planned question.	
	It places your selected detail in context.	
	It confirms that the detail you have selected gives an accurate impression of the situation.	

(2) Write 🖉 your answer in the spaces in the exam-style question above.

Review your skills

Check up

Review your response to the exam-style question on page 29. Tick ✓ the column to show how well you think you have done each of the following.

	Had a go ✓	Nearly there ✓	Got it! ✓
selected a detail that relates to the topic in the exam-style question	☐	☐	☐
framed a source enquiry question that relates to my chosen detail and the topic in the exam-style question	☐	☐	☐
chosen a specific type of source that supports my planned source enquiry question	☐	☐	☐
explained how my source would help answer my question	☐	☐	☐

Look over all of your work in this unit. Note down ✐ three things you have learned that you will apply when following up a source.

① ....

② ....

③ ....

Need more practice?

On separate paper, try ✐ the exam-style question below.

Exam-style question

Study Source B on page 21.

How could you follow up Source B to find out more about the effectiveness of treatments for the problems of ill health arising from the trench environment?

In your answer, you must give the question you would ask and the type of source you could use.

(4 marks)

How confident do you feel about each of these **skills**? Colour in ✐ the bars.

① How do I decide on a source enquiry? ☐☐☐☐

② How do I plan a source enquiry? ☐☐☐☐

③ How can I ensure my source supports the question? ☐☐☐☐

④ Answering relevantly

This unit will help you to answer a question using relevant material, which is important for all History questions. For a comparison question, it will help you to write a short answer. The skills you will build are to:

- read a question carefully to help identify a relevant point
- select information that supports your point, and is relevant to the topic and the timeframes in the question
- plan an answer, so that your explanation relates to the question.

In the exam, you will be asked to tackle questions such as the ones below. This unit will prepare you to write your own response to this type of question.

Exam-style question

Explain **one** way in which surgical treatment in Britain in the thirteenth century was different from surgical treatment in Britain in the nineteenth century.   **(4 marks)**

Exam-style question

Explain **one** way in which government approaches to the prevention of disease during the seventeenth century were different from government approaches to the prevention of disease during the nineteenth century.   **(4 marks)**

The three key questions in the **skills boosts** will help you to generate ideas for answering with relevant material.

 1 How do I read the question?

 2 How do I select relevant information?

 3 How do I plan my answer to ensure it answers the question?

The key to good comparisons is to *explain* them rather than simply *describe* them.

- Describe: give a piece of information about the topic in the question from within the timeframe in the question.
- Explain: make a clear comparison, stating how the two pieces of information are similar or how they differ.

(1) Look at the two student answers below. Tick (✓) which one describes a difference in surgical treatment between the 13th and 19th centuries and which one explains it.

Student answer	Describes (✓)	Explains (✓)
A One difference is the level of pain patients experienced. In the 13th century there was no pain relief, but in the 19th century anaesthetic was developed. This meant the level of pain was reduced.		
B In the 13th century, there was no pain relief and patients were conscious during treatment. In the 19th century, anaesthetic was developed.		

(2) For this type of question, you need to use the language of comparison. Highlight (✏) the word used to indicate difference in the student answers above. Use the table below to help you.

Similarity words	Difference words
still, remained, continued	but, however, whereas

(3) Each student answer below is about a similarity or difference. Cross out (c̶a̶t̶) a word or group of words in each answer and replace them (✏) with a word or phrase that more clearly signals a similarity or difference.

A | Disease was prevented by driving off miasma by leaving rubbish on the street in medieval times. It was prevented by burning barrels of tar during cholera epidemics in the 19th century.

B | Hospitals provided care for the ill in medieval times. They provided surgical treatment for them in the 19th century.

C | People thought an imbalance of the Four Humours caused disease in medieval times and Thomas Sydenham argued in the 17th century that it was caused by external factors.

D | People believed that God had sent the Black Death. They believed he sent the Great Plague.

E | Victims of certain diseases were quarantined. Lepers were isolated in lazar houses in medieval times and smallpox sufferers in poxhouses during the 17th century.

F | Physicians attempted to cure disease using effective metal cures in the 17th century and antibiotic cures in the 20th century.

Surgery and approaches to the prevention of disease

This unit uses the theme of surgical treatment and approaches to the prevention of disease to build your skills in answering relevantly. If you need to review your knowledge of this theme, work through these pages.

1) Sort ✏ the answers below into the timeline, which describes the key features of surgical treatment between c1250 and the present.

Microsurgery allows the first successful kidney transplants to be performed.	Black Death sufferers are weakened by the use of bloodletting by surgeons.

Universities begin to teach William Harvey's ideas about the circulation of blood.	England has about 1,100 hospitals, but most offer no surgical treatment.

Joseph Lister experiments with the use of carbolic acid as an antiseptic.	The NHS is set up, giving people access to advanced surgical treatments.

Joseph Lister experiments with the use of carbolic acid as an antiseptic.

James Simpson discovers chloroform is an effective anaesthetic.

Barber surgeons bleed their patients.	c1250	
	1348	
	1500	
	1543	Vesalius publishes 'On the Fabric of the Human Body', improving understanding of anatomy.
	1673	
	1847	
	1865	
	1948	
	1956	
	c1970s	MRI and CT scans give surgeons better internal scans of the body.

② Draw 🖉 lines linking each surgeon to the statement that matches their time period.

A 13th-century barber surgeon	a I am aware of germ theory and know it is important to use antiseptic spray to prevent infection.
B 17th-century licensed surgeon	b I have lots of advanced technology, like endoscopes and robotic machinery, to help me operate.
C 19th-century professional surgeon	c I am a surgeon who specialises in bloodletting.
D 20th-century professional surgeon	d I trained at university, using books by Vesalius and Harvey, so I know a lot about anatomy.

③ Tick ✓ the correct period that each of these statements about government approaches to the prevention of disease belong to.

	16th and 17th centuries ✓	19th century ✓	20th and 21st centuries ✓
A Around 1,300 miles of new sewers are built in London.			
B Mass vaccinations are available for diphtheria, polio, tetanus, rubella and measles.			
C Local governments issue orders to quarantine plague sufferers.			
D Henry VIII closes down bathhouses to stop the spread of syphilis.			
E The government makes the smallpox vaccination compulsory.			
F Clean Air Acts are introduced to protect people from air pollution.			
G Charles II bans large gatherings of people to limit the spread of plague.			
H A second Public Health Act is introduced to improve hygiene in cities.			
I Campaigns, like Change4Life, aim to improve people's diet.			

④ Write 🖉 definitions of these terms about government approaches to the prevention of disease.

a Quarantine ....

b Searcher ....

c Vaccination ....

d Laissez-faire ....

e Lifestyle campaign ....

① How do I read the question?

For a question about comparison between time periods, you need to pick out its key features to ensure you answer it with relevant information and analysis.

> **Exam-style question**
>
> Explain **one** way in which surgical treatment in Britain in the thirteenth century was different from surgical treatment in Britain in the nineteenth century. **(4 marks)**

① First, consider what you are being asked to do. In the exam-style question above:

   a Underline (A) the command word.

Give, describe or explain are used in Paper 1.

   b Highlight (🖉) the concept: similarity or difference.

② Next, work out how much you are supposed to do. Circle (A) the references to the size of the answer.

This could be the number of features you are expected to identify or the number of marks the question is worth.

③ Finally, find out what your answer should be about. Annotate (🖉) the exam-style question identifying:

   a the topic focus

   b the timeframes.

Remember, a good answer will:
- focus on the concept
- give information about the topic focus and be within the timeframes
- follow the command word in the exam-style question.

④ Compare these two student answers, working out which student has answered the exam-style question correctly. (🖉)

Student A

One difference was the amount of pain people experienced during surgery. In the 13th century, untrained barber surgeons performed operations on conscious patients. In the 19th century, surgeons could use anaesthetic to put their patients to sleep. This shows a difference, as patients would receive treatment that was not so rushed, with pain relief, in the 19th century compared to the 13th century.

Student B

One difference was the amount of pain people experienced during surgery. In the 13th century, untrained barber surgeons performed operations on conscious patients. In the 20th century, surgery was more precise, using techniques like laparoscopic surgery. This changed because of developments in technology.

The stronger student answer is ....

because ....

....

....

....

....

A short answer question requires you to select precise information that supports your comparison. To do this, it needs to be relevant to the topic and the timeframe.

Exam-style question

> Explain **one** way in which surgical treatment in Britain in the thirteenth century was different from surgical treatment in Britain in the nineteenth century. **(4 marks)**

(1) To unpick the exam-style question, first circle Ⓐ which one of the two concepts in the table applies to the question. Complete 🖉 the table with the topic focus and timeframes.

Concept:	Similarity / Difference
Topic:	
Timeframe 1:	
Timeframe 2:	

(2) Think of some ideas for areas of comparison related to the topic focus. Choose ✓ two that are relevant from the list below and write 🖉 two more.

success rates	☐	medicines available	☐
role of religion	☐	risk of infection	☐

....

....

(3) Highlight 🖉 one of your areas of comparison from above. Then circle Ⓐ one piece of information that relates to it from each period.

13th-century surgery	19th-century surgery
Some patients died from blood loss during bloodletting procedures.	The discovery of germ theory by Louis Pasteur encouraged surgeons to create a germ-free environment.
Barber surgeons had no knowledge that germs caused disease.	Trained surgeons could perform operations quickly, reducing the rate of blood loss.
Barber surgeons were poorly qualified to perform surgery.	Joseph Lister discovered that carbolic acid could act as an antiseptic.

(4) Complete 🖉 the final row of the table (from (3)) below, making sure that the second column shows a similarity to or difference from the first.

13th-century surgery	19th-century surgery
Patients did not usually receive surgical treatment in a hospital.	

3 How do I plan my answer to ensure it answers the question?

In order to plan a response to ensure it answers the question, you need to identify a point of comparison, support it with evidence and explain how the two things are similar or different.

Explain **one** way in which surgical treatment in Britain in the thirteenth century was different from surgical treatment in Britain in the twentieth century. (4 marks)

(1) Below is a flow diagram showing the steps you can take to planning an answer to an exam-style question like the one above.

Identify the concept, topic focus and timeframes.	→	Think of one point of comparison.	→	Select a piece of information, from your own knowledge, for each period.

a Highlight 🖉 the concept, topic focus and time frame in the question.

b Write 🖉 one point of comparison. ....

c Write 🖉 two pieces of supporting information. ....

....

....

(2) Use the thought process above to write 🖉 a plan for an answer to the exam-style question above.

> State one way in which the two timeframes are similar or different.
>
> Identify the first period and give one piece of information.
>
> Identify the second period and give one piece of information.

To complete your answer, you need to explain the similarity or difference. Some ideas that could help build an explanation are shown below.

Similarity: This shows...	Difference: This shows...
the dominance of one idea or institution	a fundamental change in a scientific idea
conservative attitudes in society	a change in the power of an institution or its approach
lack of progress in technology	a shift of attitudes in society
	advances in technology

(3) Now write 🖉 an explanation for the similarities or differences you wrote in (2).

This shows ....

....

....

....

....

Sample response

Now you have improved your ability to answer a question with relevant detail and explanation, have a go at comparing a weak and a strong student response.

Exam-style question

> Explain **one** way in which government approaches to the prevention of disease during the seventeenth century were similar to government approaches to the prevention of disease in the nineteenth century.
>
> (4 marks)

Study these two student answers to the exam-style question.

Student 1 (strong)

> One similarity between the 17th and 19th centuries was what the government tried to prevent. In the 17th century, local government officials burned bonfires in the streets to mask bad smells and purify the air during the Great Plague. In the 19th century, they still burned barrels of tar during the cholera epidemics. This shows that the government was still trying to purify the air and prevent miasma in the 19th century.

Student 2 (weak)

> One similarity between the 17th and 19th centuries was what the government believed about disease. In the medieval period, miasma was a popular theory that suggested bad smells caused disease. In the 17th century, the government still believed in miasma. They were worried that dogs, cats, litter and sewage made the problem worse. In the 19th century, the General Board of Health believed cholera was caused by miasma. They rejected John Snow's work, which suggested it was to do with the water supply. The board used evidence from the water to try and disprove his work. The beliefs stayed the same, because miasma was such a powerful idea.

① Annotate the strong answer by underlining (A) an example of each of the following features, then writing (✏) a label (A, B, C and D) for each underlined section to indicate the feature used.

   A Makes a comparison focused on the correct concept: similarity or difference.

   B Uses information from the correct timeframes.

   C Contains one piece of information from each timeframe in the exam-style question.

   D Explains briefly how the pieces of information are similar or different.

② Now underline (A) and annotate (✏) the weak answer in the same way. Look out for these mistakes:

   A The comparison does not focus on the topic in the exam-style question.

   B It uses irrelevant detail that is outside its timeframe.

   C It uses irrelevant detail that is unfocused on the exam-style question.

   D It provides too much detail, rather than selecting it precisely.

   E It explains why they are similar or different, rather than how.

Your turn!

Now it's your turn to try to answer an exam-style question.

Exam-style question

Explain **one** way in which government approaches to the prevention of disease during the seventeenth century were different from government approaches to the prevention of disease during the nineteenth century.

(4 marks)

(1) Complete the question analysis table, first circling Ⓐ which one of the two concepts applies to the question. Complete ✎ the table with the topic focus and timeframes.

Concept:	Similarity / Difference
Topic:	
Timeframe 1:	
Timeframe 2:	

(2) To help keep your answer short and to the point, try writing an answer to the exam-style question by completing the writing frame below. Using the elements you identified in (1), complete ✎ the sentence starters.

One way in which (topic focus) .... was similar/different

was ....

In (period one) ...., (first detail) ....,

....

In (period two) ...., (second detail) ....

This shows ....

....

....

....

....

....

....

....

....

....

....

....

....

Review your skills

Check up

Review your response to the exam-style question on page 39. Tick ✓ the column to show how well you think you have done each of the following.

	Had a go ✓	Nearly there ✓	Got it! ✓
read the question carefully, so my point refers to the correct concept	☐	☐	☐
selected information that supports my point, is relevant to the topic focus and matches the timeframes in the exam-style question	☐	☐	☐
planned my answer, so that my explanation shows how the information is similar or different	☐	☐	☐

Look over all of your work in this unit. Note down ✐ three things you have learned that you will apply when answering questions relevantly.

① ....

② ....

③ ....

Need more practice?

On separate paper, try ✐ the exam-style question below.

Exam-style question

Explain **one** way in which government approaches to the prevention of disease during the seventeenth century were different from government approaches to the prevention of disease during the twentieth century.

(4 marks)

How confident do you feel about each of these **skills**? Colour in ✐ the bars.

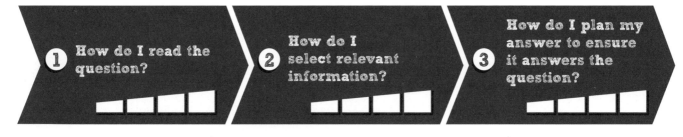

① How do I read the question?

② How do I select relevant information?

③ How do I plan my answer to ensure it answers the question?

⑤ Selecting and using supporting evidence

This unit will help you to select and use information precisely in answers focused on causation. The skills you will build are to:

- select information about different aspects of the topic in the question
- check that the information selected can be focused on the concept in the question
- use your own information to show understanding of the characteristics of the period in the question.

In the exam, you need to select and use information precisely. This helps to demonstrate that you have a wide-ranging knowledge of the topic from which you can pick and choose. This unit will help you to prepare your own response to this type of question.

Exam-style question

Explain why there were changes in the quality of hospital care during the period c1900 to the present day.

You may use the following in your answer:

- high-tech medical treatment
- the NHS

You **must** also use information of your own. (12 marks)

Exam-style question

Explain why government involvement in the prevention of disease changed quickly during the period c1800–c1900.

You may use the following in your answer:

- smallpox vaccination
- cholera epidemics

You **must** also use information of your own. (12 marks)

The three key questions in the **skills boosts** will help you to improve your ability to select and use information.

① How do I select information to answer the question?

② How do I ensure that information is relevant to the concept focus?

③ How do I use my own information?

To write a strong answer, you need to demonstrate wide-ranging knowledge and understanding. The information you select should be as specific as possible.

(1) Link 🖉 the general information about government involvement in the prevention of disease between c1800 and c1900 to specific information.

General information	Specific information
A There was a serious smallpox epidemic in the 1800s.	**a** John Snow spoke to a parliamentary committee about the cause of cholera.
B The government made people have the vaccine.	**b** Between 1837 and 1840, a smallpox epidemic killed 35,000 people.
C Some doctors had the job of vaccinating the public.	**c** The Public Health Act of 1875 was passed to provide clean water and sanitation.
D Lots of powerful people and groups resisted the smallpox vaccination.	**d** Public vaccinators were appointed in 1871.
E New sewers were built in London.	**e** In 1852, the government passed a law making the vaccination compulsory.
F The government passed a law to clean up the water supply.	**f** The Royal Society and Church spoke out against the smallpox vaccine.
G An expert advised the government on the prevention of cholera.	**g** A new sewer system for London was designed by Joseph Bazalgette.

(2) Identify some examples of specific information from (1) and write them 🖉 in the table below.

A date: a year that an event, development or individual action took place in.	
An individual or group: a named person, group or institution.	
A named development: a new idea, discovery or law.	
A statistic: a number of deaths, those treated or the cost of something.	

(3) The student answer below has used general information to explain why government involvement changed quickly. Using specific information shows more knowledge and understanding. Cross out any general information and replace 🖉 it with specific information.

> One reason government involvement changed quickly was that there were now actions the government could take to stop disease. There had been some serious epidemics in the 19th century. Some could have been prevented by new vaccinations. This led to rapid change because the government could give its support to vaccination programmes.

Medicine and the government c1800–present

This unit uses the theme of medicine and the role of the government to build your skills in selecting and using supporting evidence. If you need to review your knowledge of this theme, work through these pages.

(1) Draw ✎ lines to link the events or developments below to their impact on beliefs about the causes of disease or illness.

Event/development

A John Snow proved that cholera was waterborne in 1854–55.

B There was a rise in the number of skin cancer cases in the late 20th century.

C In 1950, the British Medical Research Council proved the link between smoking and lung cancer.

D Pasteur began work on germ theory in 1861, publishing his ideas in 1878.

Impact on beliefs

a People rejected the idea of miasma and spontaneous generation.

b People accepted that lifestyle factors could increase the risk of developing illness.

(2) Were the impacts on beliefs above gradual or rapid changes? Explain why. ✎

....

....

....

(3) Tick ✓ to show whether these statements about advances in diagnosis and medicine are true or false. Cross out ~~sat~~ and correct ✎ the false statements.

		true	false
a	Blood tests, the ability to measure blood pressure and blood sugar monitors were all developed in the 20th century.	☐	☐
b	MRI scans use magnets, CT scans use sound and ultrasound scans use advanced X-rays to build up a picture of the body.	☐	☐
c	Salvarsan 606 was discovered by Hata, Prontosil by Domagk and M&B 693 by British scientists.	☐	☐
d	Streptomycin was the first true antibiotic because it was created using microorganisms.	☐	☐
e	Florey and Chain developed penicillin into a usable treatment in 1940.	☐	☐
f	The provision of drugs was improved in the 19th century through mass production of pills, hypodermic needles and the use of insulin pumps.	☐	☐

Unit 5 Selecting and using supporting evidence 43

4 Decide whether each of the following is a method of prevention or treatment for disease and illness. Write 🖉 P or T in each box.

a | The ban on tobacco advertising in 2005. | ☐

b | The use of X-rays in radiotherapy during the 20th century. | ☐

c | Machines to replace the functions of the kidney or heart used during the 20th and 21st centuries. | ☐

d | The second Public Health Act in 1875, improving water supply and drainage. | ☐

e | The use of microsurgery techniques in kidney transplants (1956) and liver and heart transplants (1967). | ☐

f | The use of robots during brain surgery in the 20th and 21st centuries. | ☐

g | The Clean Air Acts of 1956 and 1968 in response to London smog. | ☐

h | The provision of chemotherapy drug treatments for lung cancer patients. | ☐

i | The Change4Life campaign in the early 21st century to encourage healthy eating and exercise. | ☐

j | Mass vaccination campaigns for diphtheria, polio, tetanus, rubella and measles in the 20th century. | ☐

5 Number 🖉 the following events about government involvement in the prevention of disease, placing them in chronological order.

A | The government launches the NHS. | ☐

F | The government sets up the Ministry of Health. | ☐

B | The government introduces a mass vaccination campaign for diphtheria. | ☐

G | The government bans smoking in all public places. | ☐

C | A parliamentary committee listens to John Snow's evidence about cholera. | ☐

H | Work on the London sewer system, planned by Joseph Bazalgette, finishes. | ☐

D | A cholera epidemic, leading to 20,097 deaths between 1853 and 1854, encourages John Snow to investigate its cause. | ☐

I | The government introduces the Change4Life campaign. | ☐

E | The government makes inoculation for smallpox a crime. | ☐

J | The smallpox vaccination is made compulsory by the government. | ☐

1 How do I select information to answer the question?

To plan a strong answer, you need to select and write about information from at least three aspects of the topic that demonstrate a wide-ranging knowledge of the topic.

Exam-style question

Explain why there were changes in the quality of hospital care during the period c1900 to the present day.

You may use the following in your answer:

- high-tech medical treatment
- the NHS

You **must** also use information of your own. (12 marks)

(1) Underline (A) the topic focus in the exam-style question above and circle (A) the timeframe.

(2) To get a wide range of information, you need to explore different aspects of the topic. Complete (✐) the second column in the table below for the other two aspects. One has been done for you.

Generic category	Topic aspect that links to this	Specific information about this aspect
Institutions (Hint: look at the bullet points)	The NHS	• NHS introduced in 1948 • Government ran 1,143 voluntary hospitals • Managed hospitals through regional hospital boards
Technology (Hint: look at the bullet points)		
Science (Hint: what else do people receive in hospital?)		

(3) Add (✐) two or three pieces of specific information into the final column of the table.

(4) Highlight (✐) one specific piece of information in each row, ensuring the three you choose come from different points in the timeframe. This is the evidence you could structure each of your paragraphs around.

2 How do I ensure that information is relevant to the concept focus?

An 'Explain why…' question focuses on the concept of *causation*. This means that the information you select must be able to explain *why* something happened, like change/continuity or slow/rapid change.

Below is a student's plan containing five pieces of information they would like to include in their answer to the exam-style question on page 45.

(1) Read the following statements and using the letters T (technology), I (institutions) and S (science), annotate ✏ one statement from each of the following aspects of the topic: technology, institutions and science.

> A In the late 20th century, surgeons began to use robotics to perform operations on the brain.
> B In 1919, the government set up the Ministry of Health.
> C In the 1940s, hospital doctors began to prescribe penicillin to treat patients.
> D In 1956, the first successful kidney transplant was performed using microsurgery.
> E The government set up the NHS in 1948, establishing regional hospital boards to run hospitals.

Try to cover most of the timeframe with your choices.

(2) To check that the information you choose is relevant to the concept focus:

a Underline Ⓐ the concept in the exam-style question: this will always be 'why' for question 4 on Paper 1.

b Tick ✓ what you are being asked to explain from the list.

Checklist Criteria	✓
Why a change occurred	
Why there was rapid/quick change	
Why there was slow/little change	
Why a factor decreased or increased in importance	

Now you know the concept focus, you can check whether the information can address it. The student has tried to do this with aspect C in three different ways.

(3) Circle Ⓐ the sentence of explanation that addresses the concept focus you ticked.

> Answer 1: This led to rapid change as it could be used on a national scale.

> Answer 2: This resulted in hospitals becoming more important places in the medical care-giving process.

> Answer 3: This meant patients could receive care for a greater range of illnesses.

(4) Create ✏ your own explanation, like the one you circled above, for another piece of information you selected in the list A–E in the student plan.

......

Remember: if it cannot be explained in relation to the question, then it is not relevant to the concept focus.

3 How do I use my own information?

To write a high-quality answer, you need to use information of your own about a different aspect of the topic to those suggested by the stimulus bullet points in the exam question.

Exam-style question

Explain why there were changes in the quality of hospital care during the period c1900 to the present day.

You may use the following in your answer:

- high-tech medical treatment
- the NHS

You **must** also use information of your own. (12 marks)

(1) Underline (A) the topic focus and circle (A) the timeframe in the exam-style question.

(2) Write (✏) the bullet points from the exam-style question into the table below alongside the appropriate generic category.

Generic category	Aspect of topic in the exam-style question
Individuals	
Institutions	
Science	
Technology	
Attitudes in society	

(3) Add (✏) another aspect of the topic to one of the generic categories in the table.

(4) You need to ensure that information about your chosen aspect will support your argument.
A student has written two examples for the bullet points in the exam-style question. Try (✏) doing this with the aspect you added in (3).

The NHS	The NHS used government money to improve the quality of care.
High-tech medical treatment	Hospitals were able to provide more effective treatments.

(5) Now select precisely, from your own knowledge, some specific information to support each point. One has been done for you. (✏)

Cause (Point)	Information (Evidence)
The NHS used government money to improve the quality of care in hospitals.	The NHS was set up in 1948, using taxpayers' money to provide hospital care that was free at the point of use and so available to a wider range of people, especially women.

Sample response

A well-written paragraph in a causation essay will use information that has been selected precisely from a wide range of knowledge. Studying the differences between a strong and weak student answer will help you to write your own.

Exam-style question

Explain why government involvement in the prevention of disease changed quickly during the period c1800–c1900.

You may use the following in your answer:

- smallpox vaccination
- cholera epidemics

You **must** also use information of your own.

(12 marks)

(1) Read the table below, which describes features of a strong and weak student answer.

Features of a strong student answer	Features of a weak student answer
Information selected is precise: it is relevant to the point.	Information selected is imprecise: it is only partly relevant to the point.
The concept is focused on: it gives a reason for quick change.	The concept is not focused on: it shows what the changes were, rather than explaining why they happened quickly.

a Underline (A) the precise information in the strong answer and annotate (✏) where the concept is focused on.

b Underline (A) the imprecise information in the weak answer and double underline (A) where the concept is not focused on.

Student A

One reason government involvement in the prevention of disease changed quickly was the number of serious cholera epidemics. In 1853–54, there was an epidemic that led to over 20,000 deaths in England and Wales. This prompted an investigation by John Snow, who demonstrated that the spread of cholera was to do with the contaminated water supply. This meant that the water supplies would have to be cleaned up in order to prevent another epidemic. As a result the resistance to the idea of government taking action was reduced and this led to the passing of the Public Health Act in 1875. This was a quick change in government involvement, because the epidemic created pressure on the government to force local councils to clean up the water supply.

Student B

One reason government involvement in the prevention of disease changed was that there were serious cholera epidemics. There were several outbreaks of cholera in the 19th century and scientists had begun to prove they were either due to miasma or a problem with the water supply. This shows that there were more serious disease problems in British cities in the 19th century. This led the government's role in the prevention of disease to change quickly.

c Using your answers to **a** and **b**, explain which student answer is the strongest and why.

....

....

Your turn!

This unit has focused on planning an answer. Now it's your turn to try to plan an answer to an exam-style question.

Exam-style question

Explain why government involvement in the prevention of disease changed quickly during the period c1800–c1900.

You may use the following in your answer:

- smallpox epidemic
- the work of John Snow

You **must** also use information of your own. (12 marks)

1 **a** To start the planning process, one of the bullet points from the exam-style question has been added to the table below. Write ✏ the remaining bullet point in the appropriate place in the second column, then add ✏ a topic aspect of your own alongside the relevant generic category.

Generic category	Aspect of topic in the question	Specific information
Individuals		
Institutions		
Science		
Technology		
Attitudes in society	Smallpox epidemic	

b Add ✏ one piece of specific information to each of your topic aspects.

c Check ✓ your specific information meets each of the criteria in the checklist below. Add ✏ more detail to the table in **a** if it does not.

Checklist	✓
They each cover a different aspect of the topic in the question.	
They are specific details, such as dates, individuals, named developments or statistics.	
They each come from a different point in the timeframe.	

d Identify the concept in the exam-style question. In the list below, tick ✓ what you are being asked to explain. Then tick ✓ each of your three pieces of specific information in the table in **a** to confirm they focus on this.

Why a change occurred	☐	Why there was slow/little change	☐
Why there was rapid/quick change	☐	Why a factor decreased or increased in importance	☐

2 Turn your information into a plan. Write ✏ three causes (points) in answer to the exam-style question that each piece of information in your table could support.

Cause (Point)	Information (Evidence)

Review your skills

Check up

Review your response to the exam-style question on page 49. Tick ✓ the column to show how well you think you have done each of the following.

	Had a go ✓	Nearly there ✓	Got it! ✓
selected information precisely to support the points I have made	☐	☐	☐
ensured that the information is used to explain why something happened	☐	☐	☐
used my own information to enhance my explanation, showing I understand the characteristics of the period	☐	☐	☐

Look over all of your work in this unit. Note down ✐ three things you have learned that you will apply when selecting and using supporting evidence.

① ....

② ....

③ ....

Need more practice?

On separate paper, try ✐ the exam-style question below.

Exam-style question

Explain why government involvement in the prevention of disease changed quickly during the period c1900 to the present day.

You may use the following in your answer:

• the NHS

• government lifestyle campaigns

You **must** also use information of your own.

(12 marks)

How confident do you feel about each of these **skills**? Colour ✐ in the bars.

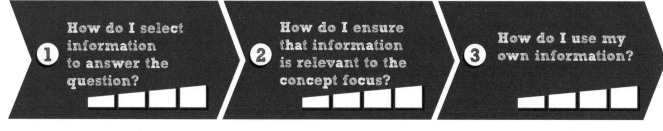

1 How do I select information to answer the question?

2 How do I ensure that information is relevant to the concept focus?

3 How do I use my own information?

6 Analysing causation

This unit will help you to plan and write better arguments when you are working on causation essays, which explain why an event or development occurred. The skills you will build are to:

- identify causes that relate to the question
- use knowledge to strengthen your arguments
- make effective links back to the question.

In the exam, causation can appear in questions 4, 5 and 6. However, causation will *always* be the focus of question 4. This unit will prepare you to write your own response to this type of question.

The three key questions in the **skills boosts** will help you to write a strong causation argument.

1 How do I build a causal argument?

2 How do I support my causal argument with my own knowledge?

3 How do I link my causal argument back to the question?

The focus of this unit is on improving your causal arguments. This will build on your understanding of good paragraph structure to write a strong causation essay.

(1) Draw (✎) lines linking the paragraph feature to its purpose in a causal argument.

A Point	**a** Explore how the evidence proves the point it supports.
B Evidence	**b** Link back to the question, explaining how the cause analysed in the paragraph relates to the question.
C Explanation	**c** Introduce the cause, providing an answer to the question.
D Link	**d** Supporting knowledge that can prove the point being made.

This unit will refer to a number of terms used to describe the components of a causation essay. These are:

A | Topic focus: the topic in the question.

B | Cause: the reason something occurred.

C | Precise information: facts, figures and dates.

D | Contextual knowledge: background information about the period, country or world view.

E | Link: a connection between causes, or between a cause and the thing you are trying to explain.

(2) Referring to the exam-style question on page 51, label (✎) each of the statements below with the appropriate term, A–E, from the list above.

a The Theory of the Four Humours, supported by the Church ☐

b Medieval treatments ☐

c Attitudes in society ☐

d Most people accepted the Church's teachings ☐

e Conservative attitudes caused people to rely on old treatments rather than accept changes to them ☐

Medicine in medieval England

This unit uses the theme of medicine in medieval England to build your skills in analysing causation. If you need to review your knowledge of this theme, work through these pages.

1 In the table below, look at the list of medieval beliefs about the causes of disease, approaches to treatment and prevention of disease. Tick ✓ which category each belief belongs in.

	Cause	Treatment	Prevention
A God sent disease as a punishment.			
B People followed the *regimen sanitates*.			
C The Four Humours were out of balance.			
D Bloodletting to balance the humours.			
E Bad air, or miasma, transmitted disease.			
F Regular attendance at Church services.			
G Going on a pilgrimage to make up for sin.			
H A moderate diet.			
I Taking a herbal remedy, like theriaca.			
J A bad alignment of the planets.			
K Having a bath to dissolve blockages in the humours.			
L Purifying the air of miasmata.			

2 Draw 🖉 lines linking each idea about disease to the treatment used.

A Disease was a punishment for sin.	a Take or apply treatments, like herbal remedies, at the right time.
B Astrology influenced a person's health.	b Bathe, purge your body or have your blood let.
C The Theory of the Four Humours.	c Go on a pilgrimage to a shrine.
D Miasma spread disease.	d Take strong-smelling herbs.

3 Complete 🖉 the text using the words in the box to help you.

criticised	Latin	conservative	soul	monasteries	classical

> The ideas that medieval people had about medicine were influenced by a range of factors. Firstly,
> .... ideas were very influential. Both Hippocrates, who came up with the
> Theory of the Four Humours, and Galen, who devised the Theory of Opposites, were popular. Their
> works had been translated into .... and were widely available in medieval
> universities.
> Another powerful influence was the Church. The Church taught that everything in nature had a
> purpose and that people had a .... This agreed with Galen's ideas. As a
> result, the Church, which controlled the production of books in its .... ,
> promoted the ideas of Galen and Hippocrates, rather than publishing new ideas.
> Finally, medieval people had a .... attitude towards science and medicine.
> They expected their physicians to be familiar with Hippocrates and Galen. Even those,
> like Henri de Mondeville, who .... classical thinkers, still had to use their
> ideas for treatment if they hoped to find work.

4 Write 🖉 the type of medical practitioner that each of the people in the table would be most likely to visit during the medieval period.

Type of person	What type of medical practitioner would they visit?
A A rich person who wanted someone to use classical ideas to diagnose their illness.	
B A merchant who wanted a herbal remedy.	
C A peasant who needed to have their blood let to rebalance their humours.	
D A rich person who wanted a broken limb set properly.	
E A very poor person who needed someone to look after them during an illness.	

5 The Black Death reached England in 1348. Tick ✓ whether the following statements about treatments and preventions for it are true or false.

		true	false
a	People prayed to God to help recover from the Black Death.	☐	☐
b	Bleeding and purging helped people to recover from the Black Death.	☐	☐
c	Physicians and surgeons lanced a patient's buboes.	☐	☐
d	People thought that carrying a posy of flowers to ward off miasma would not prevent the Black Death.	☐	☐
e	There were no attempts made by the government to quarantine Black Death sufferers.	☐	☐

How do I build a causal argument?

In order to build a causal argument, you need to identify causes that answer the question. These should address the topic focus and the process of change in the question.

Exam-style question

Explain why approaches to the treatment of disease and illness changed slowly in the period c1250-c1500.

1. The first step is to understand what it is you need to explain. Underline (A) the topic focus and circle (Ⓐ) the process of change you need to explain in the exam-style question above.

2. Next you need to consider which areas, or aspects, of the topic focus need to be explored to explain the process of change. One has been identified for you in the table below. Write (✐) two more.

Different areas or aspect of focus	A Medieval people used religious treatments.
	B
	C

3. Once you understand the focus, aim to come up with three different causes of the process of change. To do this, combine the focus and process into an exam-style question statement and write (✐) them below. The first one has been done for you.

> To help you combine process and focus, follow this formulation when writing your 'questions':
> * Explain why there was [process] in [aspect of focus]...

a | Explain why there was slow change in the use of religious treatments by medieval people.

b | ....

c | ....

4. You should now provide the opening point for each of your paragraphs by answering (✐) your questions above. One has been done for you.

a | Treatment changed slowly because the Church had a strong influence on people's ideas and beliefs.

b | ....

c | ....

5. Three students have given the answers below. However, only one addresses the focus and concept in the exam-style question. Tick (✓) the correct one.

Medieval people believed hygiene was important.	☐
Few medieval medical practitioners were trained professionally.	☐
There were new translations of medical works available.	☐

2 How do I support my causal argument with my own knowledge?

In a well-written essay, knowledge will be selected precisely to support the point you are making. It can then be explained to help validate your point.

Exam-style question

Explain why approaches to the treatment of disease and illness changed slowly in the period c1250–c1500.

Relevant knowledge will link directly to the point you are making. Two points in answer to the exam-style question are given below.

(1) Add 🖉 your own evidence for the second point in the plan.

If you struggle with this process, return to Unit 5 and review what you learned there.

Point	Evidence
A Medical training was theoretical rather than practical.	Physicians used the works of Galen and Hippocrates.
B The Church influenced people's views on disease and illness.	

To use knowledge in an analytical way, it should be connected to your point. One way to do this is to use part of the wording of your point in the same sentence as your knowledge.

(2) Look at the student answer below, which uses point A. Highlight 🖉 the phrase that connects the point and the knowledge.

> One reason treatment changed slowly was that medical training was theoretical rather than practical. The theories they were trained in were developed by people like Galen and Hippocrates.

(3) Using point B, write 🖉 a sentence that links to the evidence you wrote in (1). Use a different phrase from the one in the student example above.

....

....

Your knowledge should prove a point and be followed by an explanation of how it proves this point. In a sophisticated analysis, knowledge often forms part of the explanation too.

(4) Look at the student response below for a different point.

   a Underline (A) the point (cause).

   b Circle (A) the knowledge relating to the point.

   c Double underline (A) the explanation of how the knowledge proves the point.

> One reason treatment changed slowly was that books and learning were controlled by the Church. Many physicians were clergymen, who trained at universities like Oxford and Cambridge where the study of theology was important. This meant they followed Church ideas, like using the Four Humours, as part of their treatment plan.

(5) On a separate piece of paper, using your work from activities (1)–(3), write up 🖉 point B, supported by your own knowledge, which should be explained.

3 How do I link my causal argument back to the question?

A strong causal argument will link back to the key words in the question at the end of each paragraph. This will build up your line of reasoning, showing the relevance of your ideas to the question.

Exam-style question

Explain why approaches to the treatment of disease and illness changed slowly in the period c1250–c1500.

(1) In the student's answer below:

a circle (A) where they have identified the topic and concept focus

b underline (A) where they have provided a reason in answer to the question

c double underline (A) where they have presented their own knowledge

d highlight (✐) where they have explained how their knowledge proves their point.

> One reason there was slow change in the treatment of disease and illness was that traditional approaches were valued. Physicians used astrology to help diagnose patients and star charts to prescribe treatments. This was popular because people believed that the alignment of the stars affected their lives. This led to slow change in treatment, because people would only accept treatments that agreed with their own ideas about how the universe worked.

The final stage in the construction of a paragraph is to link back to the question, explaining how a part of the focus (treatment) and process (changed slowly) came about.

(2) Annotate (✐) the link in the student answer in **(1)**.

(3) Write (✐) your own link back to the exam-style question for the paragraph below.

> One reason treatment changed slowly was that books and learning were controlled by the Church. Many physicians were clergymen, who trained at universities like Oxford and Cambridge where the study of theology was important. This meant they followed Church ideas, like using the Four Humours, as part of their treatment plan. It led to slow change in the treatment of disease and illness because ....
>
> ....
>
> ....
>
> ....

(4) Another type of link back to the question is one that links the cause you have just discussed to another one in your essay. Write (✐) a link between the second student paragraph about Church control to the first about the popularity of traditional ideas:

> The popularity of traditional approaches combined with Church control over books and learning to bring about slow change in treatment because ....
>
> ....
>
> ....
>
> ....

Sample response

It helps to know what a strong answer looks like, so that you can check whether your causation essays build effective arguments.

Read the following exam-style question and then look at the extract from a student answer.

Exam-style question

Explain why approaches to the treatment of disease and illness changed slowly in the period c1250–c1500.

You may use the following information in your answer:

- the Church
- the role of the physician

You **must** also use information of your own.

(12 marks)

> One reason why approaches changed slowly was that books and learning were controlled by the Church. It controlled the spread of information, because books were produced in monasteries. This meant that ideas the Church supported, such as those of Galen and Hippocrates, spread to medical practitioners, who used their books as the main source for their education. This led to slow change because it reinforced the influence of traditional ideas and limited the opportunity for new ones to spread.

1. The strongest features of the student answer have been highlighted, using four different colours. Write ✎ which colour represents which feature of the causal argument.

Point .... Knowledge ....

Explanation .... Link back to the question ....

It is important to remember that more than one piece of knowledge could support the same point. This should help you focus your revision on a few pieces of detailed knowledge for each topic.

2. Tick ✓ an additional piece of knowledge from the table below for the student answer.

Most people could not read. ☐

Handwritten books were very expensive. ☐

Universities relied on books copied by monks. ☐

3. Highlight ✎ one reason why the link back to the question strengthens the paragraph.

It introduces the knowledge you used.

It provides essential information to prove the point.

It helps to build up your overall argument.

Your turn!

Using the skills you have developed over this unit, you are now going to plan and write your own answer to the exam-style question below.

Explain why approaches to the treatment of disease and illness changed slowly in the period c1250–c1500.

You may use the following information in your answer:

- the Church
- the role of the physician

You **must** also use information of your own.

(12 marks)

1) Complete 🖉 the table below with your own ideas for how to answer the exam-style question above.

Point	
Supporting knowledge	
Explanation	
Link back to the question	

2) Use ✓ the checklist to review your planned paragraph.

Checklist Have you:	✓
chosen a point that refers to a cause in answer to the question?	
used supporting knowledge linked to your point?	
explained how your supporting knowledge proves your point?	
explained your link back to the question, developing your overall argument?	

3) Write 🖉 your paragraph on a separate piece of paper. Remember to:

- connect your point and knowledge together
- use more knowledge in your explanation, if it helps strengthen it
- refer to circumstances, a key part of the process and focus, or link to another cause in your link back to the question.

Review your skills

Check up

Review your paragraph response to the exam-style question on page 59. Tick ✓ the column to show how well you think you have done each of the following.

	Had a go ✓	Nearly there ✓	Got it! ✓
chosen a cause that relates directly to the focus and process in the question	☐	☐	☐
used knowledge to strengthen the argument	☐	☐	☐
written a link that builds up my overall argument in response to the question	☐	☐	☐

Look over all of your work in this unit. Note down 🖉 the three most important things to remember about how best to organise your causal arguments.

① ....

② ....

③ ....

Need more practice?

On separate paper, try 🖉 the exam-style question below.

Exam-style question

Explain why approaches to the prevention of disease and illness changed slowly in the period c1250–c1500.

You may use the following information in your answer:

- purifying the air
- religious actions

You **must** also use information of your own.

12 marks)

How confident do you feel about each of these **skills**? Colour 🖉 in the bars.

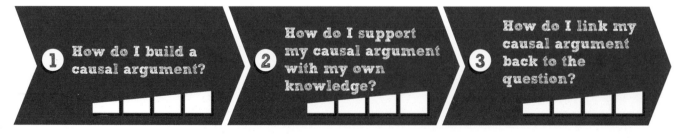

① How do I build a causal argument?

② How do I support my causal argument with my own knowledge?

③ How do I link my causal argument back to the question?

⑦ Understanding change and continuity

This unit will help you to plan and write answers to questions focused on change and continuity. The skills you will build are to:

- identify changes in a given topic over a specified timeframe
- evaluate whether an event, development or individual's work is a turning point in history
- evaluate the extent of change in a given topic over a specified timeframe.

In the exam, the 'how far do you agree' question could focus on the nature or extent of change, patterns of change, the process of change or the impact of change. This unit will help you to write a response to the first two types of question.

Exam-style question

'The invention of the printing press was a turning point in the spread of ideas about medicine in the period c1400–c1700.'

How far do you agree? Explain your answer.

You may use the following in your answer:

- Vesalius' *On the Fabric of the Human Body*
- the Royal Society

You **must** also use information of your own. (16 marks)

Exam-style question

'There was huge change in the way ideas about medicine spread in the period c1400–c1700.'

How far do you agree? Explain your answer.

You may use the following in your answer:

- the printing press
- the Royal Society

You **must** also use information of your own. (16 marks)

The three key questions in the **skills boosts** will help you to generate ideas to plan an essay focused on change and continuity.

① How do I identify change?

② How do I evaluate whether something is a turning point?

③ How can I evaluate the extent of change?

In this unit you will focus on how to construct a plan for an essay about change and continuity. However, to write this up, you still need to follow the correct paragraph structure.

1 Choose ✓ the best description of the role of each of these features in a paragraph.

Feature	Descriptions to choose from	Best description ✓
Point	To open a paragraph, focusing on one aspect of the question.	
	To open a paragraph with some description relevant to the question.	
Evidence or knowledge	To support your point with anything you can remember about the topic.	
	To support or illustrate your point with precisely selected information.	
Explanation	To explain how your information proves the point you are making.	
	To give a bit more detail about the information you have selected.	
Link back to the question	To build up your overall argument in relation to the question set.	
	To repeat, or paraphrase, the words of the question.	

Look at the student paragraph below, which is part of an answer to an exam-style question about the extent of change.

Exam-style question

'There was huge change in the way ideas about medicine spread in the period c1400–c1700.'

How far do you agree? Explain your answer.

The change in the way ideas about medicine spread was on an international scale. The printing press was developed in Germany around 1440. By 1500, there were hundreds of presses throughout Europe. This meant that many more physicians could have direct access to printed texts and the printing press enabled Vesalius' 'Fabric of the Human Body' to be widely distributed in the 16th century. This was a huge change because medical students and professionals across Europe had a new way to learn ideas about medicine and new ideas could be spread more widely and more quickly.

2 a Highlight ✏ where a point has been made.

b Underline Ⓐ where evidence has been given.

c Circle Ⓐ where an explanation has been made.

d Double underline Ⓐ where the student has linked back to the question.

3 The student has also begun to use the language of continuity and change. Label ✏ the student answer with any references to the following elements of change, using the words in bold as your labels. You may not find them all.

a the **pace** of change: how fast or slow a change is

b a **trend**: a group of similar changes continuing in the same direction

c **extent** of change: how big or small the change is

d the **direction** of change: the way change is heading, whether towards a situation improving or getting worse

Spreading ideas and preventing disease

This unit uses the theme of the spread of ideas about medicine and the government's role in the prevention of disease to build your skills in understanding change and continuity. If you need to review your knowledge of this theme, work through these pages.

1. Circle Ⓐ the correct answer to the questions about the new ideas that were spread between c1400 and c1700 below.

    a   What did Andreas Vesalius draw detailed diagrams of?

    i   Human bodies   ii   Microbes   iii   Printing presses

    b   What did William Harvey discover?

    i   The circulation of blood   ii   The printing press   iii   The microscope

    c   Harvey wrote his key book in 1628, but in what year did his ideas appear in universities?

    i   1693   ii   1673   iii   1728

    d   What did Thomas Sydenham encourage medical students to do?

    i   Read Galen and Hippocrates   ii   Treat each symptom separately

    iii   Observe patients closely to work out the disease they were suffering from

    e   Which statement best describes humanism during the Renaissance?

    i   God was responsible for everything   ii   Experimentation was pointless

    iii   People could make up their own minds about the world around them

2. Complete ✎ the sentences, giving a brief explanation of the significance of each of the discoveries and developments in ①.

    a   The work of Vesalius meant that surgeons ....
    ....

    b   The work of Harvey was not significant in the short term because ....
    ....

    c   The work of Sydenham meant that doctors ....
    ....

    d   Humanism was significant because it meant people stopped ....
    ....

(2) Draw ✎ lines to link the method used to spread ideas between c1400 and c1700 and the impact it had.

A The Church produced books and controlled universities during the medieval period.	**a** Books and pamphlets could be copied more quickly and accurately.
B The printing press was developed around 1440.	**b** New ideas from around Europe were discussed and their work published in a journal called *Philosophical Transactions*.
C University lecturers started to perform dissections as part of their teaching during the 16th century.	**c** Medical students had a more accurate understanding of human anatomy.
D The Royal Society, made up of leading scientists, met for the first time in 1660.	**d** Only ideas and books that the Church approved of were taught to medical students.

(3) Read the statements below, they are about government actions to prevent disease between c1500 and c1900. They are in chronological order. Cross out ~~cat~~ the incorrect information in each of these statements and write ✎ your own corrections beside it. Continue on a separate piece of paper if you need to.

a | Henry VIII closed down alehouses. | ....

b | Homeowners were executed if their street was dirty. | ....

c | Searchers quarantined victims of syphilis. | ....

d | The diphtheria vaccination was made compulsory. | ....

e | Bazalgette built a new sewer system in Birmingham. | ....

f | The Public Health Act (1875) improved water supplies and air and housing quality. | ....

(4) Complete ✎ the sentences, which give a brief explanation of why the government took each of the actions described in (3).

a | *To stop the spread of* ....

b | *To remove the sources of* ....

c | *To prevent the spread of the* ....

d | *To stop people developing* ....

e | *To limit waterborne bacteria infecting people with* ....

f | *To help improve people's* ....

1 How do I identify change?

For a question about change and continuity, you need to identify what has changed over the period. This will help to provide evidence for the points in your argument.

'The invention of the printing press was a turning point in the spread of ideas about medicine in the period c1400–c1700.'

How far do you agree? Explain your answer.

(1) Underline (A) the topic focus in the exam-style question above and highlight (✏) the timeframe.

(2) Summarise (✏) the state of affairs in the topic focus at the start and end of the period.

> *At the start of the period, ideas about medicine spread* ....
>
> ....
>
> ....

> *At the end of the period, ideas about medicine spread* ....
>
> ....
>
> ....

(3) Add (✏) four events, developments or the works of individuals to the table below that could have contributed to the difference described in (2). Some things that you should look for are:

- (?) changes in technology
- (?) new ideas from scientists
- (?) shifts in attitudes
- (?) examples of weakening or strengthening institutions

Development of the printing press, c1440	Weakening power of the Church	

(4) Ask yourself questions (1)–(3) again, this time focusing on changes in 'the role of the government in the prevention of disease in the period c1600–c1900'. Work through the stages on paper and then write (✏) the six changes you have decided on in the space below.

2 How do I evaluate whether something is a turning point?

To construct a plan for an essay focused on patterns of change, you need to apply criteria to decide whether an event, individual's work or development is a turning point.

Exam-style question

'The invention of the printing press was a turning point in the spread of ideas about medicine in the period c1400–c1700.'

(1) Underline Ⓐ the topic focus, highlight 🖉 the timeframe and circle Ⓐ the turning point provided in the exam-style question.

(2) Complete 🖉 the before and after table to help you analyse the turning point provided in the exam-style question. The before side has been done for you.

Before the turning point	After the turning point
a Books were copied by monks.	
b Information spread slowly.	
c The Church approved the books that were produced.	

(3) Apply criteria to help judge whether an event is a turning point. Complete 🖉 the table below, relating the generic criteria to the specific turning point in the exam-style question.

Did it affect the pace of change?	
Evidence that the pace of change sped up	Evidence that the pace of change slowed down or stayed the same

Did it break with a trend?	
Evidence that it was a major disruption in a trend	Evidence that it was part of a trend of similar changes (list other events/developments that affected the topic in the question)

Did it affect the direction of change?	
Evidence that it led to progress (things improved)	Evidence that it did not lead to progress or that things stayed the same/grew worse

(4) Turn the findings in your table into two opening statements for paragraphs in an essay by completing the sentences below. 🖉

An argument that the printing press was a turning point was that	Was it part of a trend?
However, it may not have been a turning point as	Did anything stay the same?

3 How can I evaluate the extent of change?

In order to evaluate how much has changed over a period of time, you need to identify what has changed and then use criteria to evaluate the changes.

Exam-style question

'There was huge change in the way ideas about medicine spread in the period c1400–c1700.'

How far do you agree? Explain your answer.

1 Underline Ⓐ the topic focus and highlight 🖉 the timeframe in the exam-style question.

2 Complete 🖉 the table to help you identify what changed between the start and end of the timeframe in the exam-style question above. Your points should relate to the topic focus.

State of affairs c1400	State of affairs c1700
	Ideas spread through books produced by printing presses.
	New universities were influenced by humanism.
	Popular ideas about medicine spread by word of mouth.

3 Use the questions below to help you judge the extent of change during the timeframe. Circle Ⓐ the appropriate options in the table to answer each question.

a What was the scale of the change?

| Local | | National | | International |

b What was the level of progress in the attitudes of people, the power of institutions and scientific knowledge?

| Significant progress | | No progress | | Regress |

c Draw 🖉 an arrow on the value continuum below to show how much continuity there was between the start and end of the period.

Continuity   Change
(a lot stayed the same)   (a lot changed)

1   2   3   4   5

4 Use your ideas in the table in ② to help you complete 🖉 the sentences below, which could form the plan for an essay about extent of change.

a The scale of change during this period was ....
....

b During the period there was significant ....
....

c Overall, there was .... continuity between the start and end of the period.

Unit 7 Understanding change and continuity   67

Sample response

The ability to evaluate a turning point is vital in an essay focused on patterns of change. Seeing the strengths in a strong student answer will help you when writing your own.

Exam-style question

'The invention of the printing press was a turning point in the spread of ideas about medicine in the period c1400–c1700.'

How far do you agree? Explain your answer.

Study these two paragraphs, which are part of a strong student's answer to the exam-style question above.

> The printing press sped up the spread of ideas. Before the printing press, books were produced by monks who wrote them out by hand. After the printing press was developed by Gutenberg in 1440, books could be copied by machine. For example, thousands of copies could be made of Vesalius' book 'On the Fabric of the Human Body'. This process was faster because machine production could outpace production by hand. This made the printing press a turning point, because new ideas could spread quickly across Europe, as lots of copies of new books like Vesalius' could be produced and distributed in a short space of time.
>
> However, the printing press was also part of a trend of similar changes in the spread of ideas. In the 16th century, the ideas of humanism became more influential, which encouraged a break with medieval ideas. This continued into the 17th century, when the Royal Society was set up to discuss new scientific ideas. Both of these developments meant ideas could spread because people were more willing to accept and discuss them. This suggests that printing was less of a turning point, because it was a part of a trend towards sharing ideas.

(1) Identify the skills the student has demonstrated. To do this:

   a Highlight 🖊 changes they have used as evidence: events, developments or the works of individuals.

   b Underline Ⓐ criteria for a turning point: change in pace, direction of change or disruption of a trend.

   c Circle Ⓐ references to the extent of change: scale of impact, level of continuity or progress in attitudes, power or knowledge.

(2) The student has demonstrated good understanding of change and continuity, but complete ✓ the checklist below to find out how well they have structured their paragraph.

Checklist	✓
Does it focus on the topic?	
Is the evidence from within the timeframe?	
Does the line of reasoning, developed in the link back to the question, relate to whether the turning point mentioned in the question is actually a turning point?	

Your turn!

Now it's your turn to try to answer an exam-style question.

Exam-style question

'The Great Plague was a turning point in the role of the government in the prevention of disease in the period c1500–c1900.'

How far do you agree? Explain your answer.

You may use the following in your answer:

- quarantine
- Jenner's vaccination

You **must** also use information of your own.

(16 marks)

The flow chart below will help you to construct a plan for the exam-style question.

Identify the topic focus, timeframe and proposed turning point in the question.	Make a list of the state of affairs before and after the turning point.	Apply criteria to help generate points about whether it was a turning point (consider whether other developments were more significant).	Did it affect the pace of change? Did it break with a trend (consider the whole period)? Did it affect the direction of change?

1. Write ✏ the four points you would make in your essay, each of which could start a paragraph in answer to the exam-style question.

   1 ....

   2 ....

   3 ....

   4 ....

2. Write ✏ one of your paragraphs, remembering to structure it around a point, supported by evidence, which you explain and then link back to the question.

   ....

   ....

   ....

   ....

   ....

   ....

   ....

   ....

   ....

Review your skills

Check up

Review your response to the exam-style question on page 69. Tick ✓ the column to show how well you think you have done each of the following.

	Had a go ✓	Nearly there ✓	Got it! ✓
followed a clear paragraph structure, including changes as part of my evidence	☐	☐	☐
focused on the topic, timeframe and turning point in the question	☐	☐	☐
developed a line of reasoning related to whether the suggested turning point in the question was actually a turning point	☐	☐	☐

Look over all of your work in this unit. Note down ✎ three things you have learned that you will apply when answering questions focused on change and continuity.

① ....

② ....

③ ....

Need more practice?

On separate paper, try ✎ the exam-style question below.

Exam-style question

'There was huge change in the role of the government in the prevention of disease in the period c1500–c1900.'

How far do you agree? Explain your answer.

You may use the following in your answer:

• the Great Plague
• the Public Health Act of 1875

You **must** also use information of your own.

(16 marks)

How confident do you feel about each of these **skills**? Colour ✎ in the bars.

① How do I identify change?

② How do I evaluate whether something is a turning point?

③ How can I evaluate the extent of change?

Making a judgement

This unit will help you to reach a judgement, which is justified fully, in answers about change and continuity. The skills you will build are to:

- organise the information in an essay plan to help reach a judgement
- use conflicting evidence to help modify a judgement
- weight the arguments in an essay to help make a valid judgement.

In the exam, the 'how far do you agree' question requires you to make a judgement supported by criteria (reasons) that you have built up throughout your essay. This unit will help you to plan and write your own response to this type of question.

Exam-style question

'Technology was the most important factor in improving the diagnosis of illness and disease during the nineteenth and twentieth centuries.'

How far do you agree? Explain your answer.

You may use the following in your answer:

- microscopes
- the work of Crick and Watson on DNA

You **must** also use information of your own.

(16 marks)

Exam-style question

'The work of Vesalius was the main reason why there were developments in the understanding of the human body in the period c1500–c1700.'

How far do you agree? Explain your answer.

You may use the following in your answer:

- the publication of Vesalius's *On the Fabric of the Human Body*
- William Harvey

You **must** also use information of your own.

(16 marks)

The three key questions in the **skills boosts** will help you to plan and write a judgement.

1 How do I organise information to reach a judgement?

2 How do I deal with conflicting evidence?

3 How do I make a convincing judgement?

Before you can make a judgement, you need to identify what you are being asked to make a judgement on. In the 'how far' question, you could be asked to make a judgement on:

A | the nature or extent of change: what types of change occurred or how much change there was?

B | patterns of change: the significance of a turning point

C | the process of change: the causes of change or factors affecting the pace of change

D | the impact of change: the consequences of a change

(1) Study the exam-style questions **a**–**d** below. Which type of judgement are you being asked to make in each one? Write 🖉 A, B, C or D.

a **Exam-style question**

The invention of the printing press was a turning point in the spread of ideas about medicine in the period c1400–c1700.

b **Exam-style question**

There was huge change in the way ideas about medicine spread in the period c1400–c1700.

c **Exam-style question**

Technology was the most important factor in improving the diagnosis of illness and disease during the nineteenth and twentieth centuries.

d **Exam-style question**

The work of Vesalius was the main reason why there were developments in the understanding of the human body in the period c1500–c1700.

Although this is not an essential feature, you could write an introduction to show you understand what you are being asked to make a judgement on. If you do, in a 'how far' essay it should:

• be a couple of lines long
• set out what the argument is going to be
• focus on the correct type of judgement about change (A, B, C or D).

(2) Below are some answers to the exam-style question **c** above. Tick ✓ the answer that does all three things listed in the bullet points above.

Technology provided tools for improving diagnosis, but changes in ideas and access to diagnosis methods were also important reasons.

Technology was very different at the start and end of the period. Observation by a medical expert was the main method at the start and more complex scanning technology at the end.

A turning point in diagnosis was the development of x-rays, because it could be used on a large scale and had a big impact on the success rates for surgery.

Diagnosis and anatomy

This unit uses the theme of diagnosis methods and understanding of the human body to build your skills in making a judgement. If you need to review your knowledge of this theme, work through these pages.

(1) Below is a list of developments in diagnostic technology. Write 🖊 each one into the timeline at the correct date.

Ernst Ruska and Max Knoll develop the electron microscope.	The NHS is set up, providing greater access to new methods of diagnosis.	An instrument for measuring blood pressure is first used.
Bloods tests are used for diagnosis of a wide range of illnesses and disease.	Ultrasound scans are used to look for kidney stones and gall stones.	Endoscopes are used to take pictures of the inside of the human body.
X-rays are used to find broken bones and aid surgeons.		

Leeuwenhoek develops a microscope that allows 'animalcules' to be observed.	1683	
	1880s	
Richard Petri designs the petri dish to observe bacteria.	c1887	
	1890s	
	1900s	
	1931	
	1930s	
	1940s	
	1948	
	c1970s	MRI and CT scans give surgeons better internal scans of the body.

(2) Draw 🖉 lines to link the developments in ideas about disease to their consequences.

A c1700s: The Enlightenment spreads across Europe.	**a** Diseases could be predicted more accurately.
B 1875: Dr Henry Bastian argues for continued belief in the idea of spontaneous generation.	**b** Blood or other samples could be analysed for specific germs to diagnose illness or disease.
C 1878: Louis Pasteur publishes the germ theory of infection.	**c** Hereditary diseases were better understood.
D 1882: Robert Koch discovers the bacteria that cause tuberculosis.	**d** Doctors investigated lifestyle factors to aid the diagnosis process.
E 1950s: Doctors observe the link between lung cancer and smoking.	**e** Scientists could investigate which germ caused which disease.
F 1953: James Watson and Francis Crick discover the structure of DNA.	**f** Some doctors refused to accept the link between germs and disease.
G 2000: The Human Genome project finishes mapping out its blueprint of human DNA.	**g** This encouraged scientists to experiment and find out new explanations for disease and illness.

(3) Sort ✓ each of these statements, deciding whether they relate to Andreas Vesalius (AV) or William Harvey (WH).

Statement	AV ✓	WH ✓
A He published *Six Anatomical Tables* and *On the Fabric of the Human Body*.		
B He challenged Galen, arguing that veins carry only blood.		
C He was the personal physician to Charles I.		
D He identified 300 mistakes in Galen's work on anatomy.		
E He was a lecturer in surgery at the University of Padua.		
F He wrote *An Anatomical Account of the Motion of the Heart and Blood in Animals*.		

(4) Complete 🖉 the text on the way institutions, attitudes and ideas about medicine changed between 1500 and 1700. Use the words in the box.

Sydenham	Church	fugitive	dissection	religion	humanism

In medieval times the .... had been powerful, but it split in the 1500s and its power declined. As a result, ... became more common. This also led to new forms of Christianity, which did not value highly decorated churches and books, giving artists time to draw .... sheets and illustrate medical textbooks.

The 1500 and 1600s were also a time for new ideas inspired by ...., which encouraged new ways to explain the world, moving away from .... Scientists began to challenge old ideas like the Four Humours. For example, Thomas .... argued for the separate nature of disease and Van Helmont questioned the relationship between the Four Humours and digestion.

How do I organise information to reach a judgement?

For a 'how far question', you need to organise the information in your response into points for and against the judgement in the question.

Exam-style question

'Technology was the most important factor in improving the diagnosis of illness and disease during the nineteenth and twentieth centuries.'

How far do you agree? Explain your answer.

You may use the following in your answer:

- microscopes
- the work of Crick and Watson on DNA

You **must** also use information of your own. (16 marks)

(1) Underline (A) the topic focus, circle (A) the timeframe and highlight the judgement given in the exam-style question above.

(2) Identify specific aspects of the topic in the exam-style question by filling in the second column of the table below.

You can use different aspects of the topic and/or explore the aspect referred to in the judgement in different ways.

Generic factor	Specific aspect(s) of topic in the question	✓ / ✗
Individuals		
Institutions		
Science		
Technology	Technology that improved diagnosis	✓
Attitudes in society		

(3) Complete the third column of the table above to show whether information related to this aspect could be used to support the argument for ✓ or against ✗ the judgement in the exam-style question.

(4) Use the specific aspects you've identified to generate points for a plan using the table below. For each aspect of the topic, ask yourself 'how does this support or challenge the statement in the question?'

Specific aspect	How does this support or challenge the statement in the question?	Order
Diagnosis technology	Technology helped to make diagnoses more accurate.	1

(5) Order the points that you've made into an outline essay plan using the third column of the table above, numbering them so that points for are first and points against are last.

2 How do I deal with conflicting evidence?

Some pieces of evidence that you use will conflict with one another, but if you can explain what this conflict reveals it can strengthen your answer.

Exam-style question

'Technology was the most important factor in improving the diagnosis of illness and disease during the nineteenth and twentieth centuries.'

How far do you agree? Explain your answer.

You may use the following in your answer:

* microscopes
* the work of Crick and Watson on DNA

You **must** also use information of your own.

(16 marks)

① Look at some conflicting ideas two students identified when thinking about the most important factor in improving diagnosis. Identify 🖉 one of your own on line C.

> A Was it technology or the individual who used it that improved diagnosis?
>
> B Was it new scientific ideas or support from the government that improved diagnosis?
>
> C Was it .... or .... that ....

② This page will explore conflict A. In the table below write 🖉 one piece of evidence for each side of the argument. Then explain how the evidence answers the question.

Point	It was **technology** that led to improved diagnosis.	It was the work of the **individual** who used technology that improved diagnosis.
Evidence		
Explanation		
Weight		

③ Consider the *weight* of each of these ideas. If you think one made a bigger contribution to the topic than the other, write 🖉 a + symbol under it. If you think their contribution to the topic was equal, write 🖉 an = symbol underneath both.

④ Write 🖉 down what the conflict reveals. In an essay, this would be a part of your link back to the question at the end of your second explanation.

> A link should reinforce how the point explained in a paragraph relates to the question.
> * If you wrote a + symbol underneath one idea, then explain how one <u>needed</u> the other to be significant.
> * If you wrote an = symbol underneath both, then explain how one <u>helped</u> the other to be significant.

....

....

....

....

3 How do I make a convincing judgement?

There is no such thing as a 'right' judgement. In a well-written essay, you will give a judgement showing that you have weighed up the arguments to reach a decision. The process of reaching a convincing judgement is shown in the flow chart below.

| Create a plan with points for and against. | → | Apply weight to each point, to reflect how convincing it is. | → | Reach a judgement, making clear what criteria you used to weight the arguments. |

Exam-style question

'Technology was the most important factor in improving the diagnosis of illness and disease during the nineteenth and twentieth centuries.'

How far do you agree? Explain your answer

You may use the following in your answer:

* microscopes
* the work of Crick and Watson on DNA

You **must** also use information of your own. (16 marks)

① Add a point for and against to the plan below. Your point against should relate to another factor.

A For: Technology enabled discoveries to be made that were crucial for improvements in diagnosis.

B For: ....

C Against: Institutions provided patients with access to diagnostic equipment.

D Against: ....

② Consider each point in ① and write a score reflecting how convincing you find it: up to 5 if the point strengthens the argument in support of the statement in the question, and down to –5 if it weakens it.

③ Explain the weighting for one of your points, making your criteria clear. A student answer, which could be used as part of a conclusion, is provided for the first argument.

Consider the following:
* How many people were affected?
* How important was it in helping other developments to occur?
* How reliant was it on other developments?
* How big an impact did it have on the topic focus in the judgement?

To remind yourself of criteria to help you assess, see Unit 7.

Argument	How much weight did you give it? (out of 5)	Explain your decision, referring to the statement in the question and the criteria in ②.
A	+3	Technology had a big impact on improving diagnosis, helping scientists put their ideas into practice. However, its importance is limited by its reliance on those scientists to have an impact.

Sample response

A good conclusion is an important feature of a 'how far' essay. Comparing a strong student's answer with a weaker one will help you when writing your own.

Exam-style question

'The work of individual scientists was the most important factor in improving the diagnosis of illness and disease during the nineteenth and twentieth centuries.'

How far do you agree? Explain your answer.

You may use the following in your answer:

- the work of Robert Koch
- the development of x-ray machines

You **must** also use information of your own.

(16 marks)

Study the plan below before examining the student answers in ①.

Point 1: Individual scientists developed new ideas about the causes of disease, enabling their diagnosis.

Point 2: Scientists developed technology that could be used for diagnosis.

Point 3: However, some scientists held onto old ideas.

Point 4: They also relied on improvements in technology to make their discoveries.

① Annotate 🖉 the strong and weak student conclusions below. Here are some features to look for:

Features of a strong conclusion	Features of a weak conclusion
A Use of criteria to support judgements B Direct comparison of factors C References to the argument for and against	D Unsupported assertion: a judgement without criteria to support it E Repetition of points from the essay F The use of new evidence

Strong student response:

The most important factor in improving the diagnosis of illness and disease was the work of scientists like Koch, Crick and Watson, because without their ideas about the causes of disease and how to detect it, diagnosis could not have improved and helped so many people. Their work was more important than the work of the government, because even though the founding of the NHS in 1948 helped people to access improved diagnoses, the doctors needed ideas about disease that were advanced enough for their observations to be accurate. However, even individuals slowed improvements a little, as some scientists like Bastian resisted change, but this was only temporary and their challenges were disproved. They also relied on improvements in technology, like the electron microscope, helping them make discoveries. Even so, without individual scientists to exploit the technology, diagnosis would not have improved.

Weak student response:

The work of individual scientists was the most important reason, because they were important to improvements in diagnosis. However, there were other reasons like the work of the government and advances in technology. For example, blood tests were introduced in the 1930s, making diagnosis easier. This was by scientists, who were important.

Your turn!

Now it's your turn to try to answer an exam-style question.

Exam-style question

'The work of Vesalius was the main reason why there were developments in the understanding of the human body in the period c1500–c1700.'

How far do you agree? Explain your answer.

You may use the following in your answer:

- the publication of Vesalius's *On the Fabric of the Human Body*
- William Harvey

You **must** also use information of your own. (16 marks)

1. Write 🖉 an essay plan, covering three to four points. The first one or two points must agree with the judgement in the exam-style question and the rest disagree, exploring alternative reasons.

Point 1: .... ⭘ ⭘

Point 2: .... ⭘ ⭘

Point 3: .... ⭘ ⭘

Point 4: .... ⭘ ⭘

2. a. Highlight 🖉 two conflicting points in your plan and explain on a separate piece of paper what the conflict reveals.

   b. If you think one of your highlighted points made a bigger contribution to the topic than the other, put a tick ✓ next to it.

   c. If you think their contribution to the topic was equal, place an = symbol next to them both. 🖉

3. Weight the points in your plan from −5 to +5, reflecting how convincing you find each of them. 🖉

4. Write 🖉 a conclusion, making clear the criteria (reasons) for your judgement.

....

....

....

....

....

....

....

....

....

....

Review your skills

Check up

Review your response to the exam-style question on page 79. Tick ⊘ the column to show how well you think you have done each of the following.

	Had a go ⊘	Nearly there ⊘	Got it! ⊘
organised the information in my plan around points for and against the judgement in the question	☐	☐	☐
used conflicting evidence to modify my judgement	☐	☐	☐
made a valid judgement, reflecting the weight I assigned to each of the arguments in my essay	☐	☐	☐

Look over all of your work in this unit. Note down ✎ three things you have learned that you will apply when making a judgement.

① ....

② ....

③ ....

Need more practice?

On separate paper, try ✎ the exam-style question below.

Exam-style question

'The declining power of the Church was the most important factor affecting developments in the understanding of the human body in the period c1500–c1700.'

How far do you agree? Explain your answer.

You may use the following in your answer:

- dissection
- William Harvey

You **must** also use information of your own.   (16 marks)

How confident do you feel about each of these **skills**? Colour in ✎ the bars.

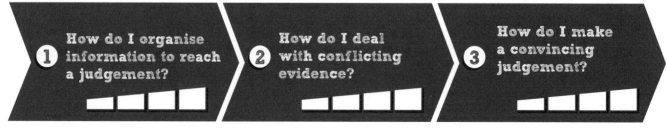

1 How do I organise information to reach a judgement?

2 How do I deal with conflicting evidence?

3 How do I make a convincing judgement?

Answers

Unit 1

Page 2

1. An argument about what the information suggests or proves.

2. **Features:** A, D, E.

   Specific details: B, C, F.

3. a. (No man's land was difficult to work in). ~~A detail that demonstrates this is that~~ stretcher bearers had to cross it under shell or machine gun fire to collect casualties.

   b. ~~One feature of the work of the RAMC is that~~ (The RAMC ran the aid posts). Their purpose was to provide emergency first aid.

   c. (The Dressing Stations had few resources). ~~From my own knowledge I know that~~ they had enough supplies and staff to look after the wounded for a week.

Page 3

1. a and b

Mistakes	Corrections
The officer at the RAP could perform an immediate operation if he thought it was necessary.	The officer at the RAP could perform first aid if he thought it was necessary.
...a Base Hospital.	...a Dressing Station.
...so that transport home could be arranged.	...so that further treatment could be provided.
...could not be operated on until the patient reached the Base Hospital.	...could be operated on at the Casualty Clearing Station.

2. **Box 2:** The army required a huge amount of staff to cope with the number of casualties.

   Box 3: The RAMC had a highly organised system for dealing with casualties.

   Box 4: The RAMC was a very effective organisation for dealing with the wounded.

Page 4

3. **True:** a, d

   False: b, c, e

4. **Box 2:** Amputation

   Box 3: Thomas Splint

   Box 4: Mobile x-ray

   Box 5: Blood bank

Page 5

1. **Topic focus:** the work of the RAMC.

2. A b; B a; C f; D c; E g; F e; G d

3. Student's own response, but it might include:

   The RAMC organised the stages of treatment.

   RAMC medical officers made the initial diagnosis.

Page 6

1. Student's own response, but you might write:

   Box 1: Medical professionals worked for the RAMC.

   Box 2:
   - One medical officer ran the Regimental Aid Post.
   - There were not enough of them to meet the huge numbers of casualties.
   - Stretcher bearers helped to transport casualties to the RAP for the RAMC.

   Box 4 (left): Understaffed.

   Box 4: (right): Role of stretcher bearers.

2. a. **Specific feature:** The RAMC worked on the frontline.

   b. **Supporting detail:** They ran the Regimental Aid Post, which was about 200 metres from the fighting.

3. Personal choice, but might include: The RAMC was made up of medical professionals. They had stretcher bearers who would transport patients from no man's land to the RAP.

4. Personal choice, but for the example given above:

   a. **Specific feature:** The RAMC was made up of medical professionals.

   b. **Supporting detail:** They had stretcher bearers who would transport patients from no man's land to the RAP.

Page 7

1. **Feature:** organised the stages of transport.

   Details: arranged the chain of evacuation; the first stage was the Regimental Aid Post, which gave immediate first aid; the Dressing Station at the second stage; the Casualty Clearing Station at the third stage.

   Explanation: it made the best use of medical personnel and ensured that troops could be treated and returned to duty, or transported home, as quickly as possible.

2. Student's own response, but you might tick:

   Do not include explanation of the feature.

   Do not include more than one piece of additional detail.

3. ~~One feature of the work of~~ the RAMC ~~was that they~~ organised the stages of treatment. ~~The organisation arranged the chain of evacuation.~~ At the first stage was the Regimental Aid Post, which gave immediate first aid. ~~This was followed by the Dressing Station at the second stage and the Casualty Clearing Station at the third stage. This was a good system, because it made the best use of medical personnel and ensured that troops could be treated and returned to duty, or transported home, as quickly as possible.~~

(4) Student's own response, but you might write: The RAMC organised the stages of treatment. They ran the Dressing Station, which was the second stage in the evacuation process.

Page 8

(1) **Feature:** treated casualties caused by the fighting.

Detail: staffed the Casualty Clearing Stations.

Detail: they could be overwhelmed when a significant battle took place.

(2) ~~Feature 1: They were helped by stretcher-bearers.~~

~~Feature 2: This could be a difficult job, as they could be overwhelmed when a significant battle took place.~~

Page 9

(1) Student's own response, but could include the following:

Environment	They were in makeshift accommodation
Fighting	Close to the frontline
Injury, disease and illness	Had to cope with all serious injuries
Logistics	Organised next stage of treatment
Diagnosis and treatment	Basic treatment provided
Types of people	Medical personnel

(2) Student's own response.

Unit 2

Page 12

(1) **Origin:** Author/creator details; **Purpose:** Why a source was created; **Provenance:** The nature, origin and purpose (NOP) of a source; **Usefulness:** What a source can be used for; **Reliability:** How much a source can be trusted; **Criteria:** A way of judging a source.

(2) Tick: A, C, D

Page 13

(1) A: a, d, g

B: e, f, j

C: c, k, l

D: b, h, i

(2) **a** Student's own response, but you might write: They transported the wounded off the battlefield.

b Student's own response, but you might write: The risk of death.

c Student's own response, but you might write: To provide first aid to get soldiers back to the frontline quickly, if possible.

d Student's own response, but you might write: It made their journey to treatment a slower and more painful one.

Page 14

(3) **a** A; **b** B; **c** A; **d** C

(4) A b; B e; C a; D f; E c; F d

Page 15

(1) **a** (Nature)   Origin

From an account by Charles Horton, who was a RAMC stretcher bearer at the Third Battle of Ypres (1917). He wrote his (recollections) in 1970.

b Tick: To recall the conditions on the Western Front.

(2) Student's own response, but you might tick: authoritative or typical.

(3) **a** and **b** Student's own response, but you might suggest that Source B is authoritative: The author of Source B had experience of working as a stretcher bearer, so is in a good position to tell us about the problems he faced.

Or you could choose a criterion that possibly weakens the usefulness of the source: it may not be typical, because he was only one stretcher bearer whose experiences may not give us a view of the problems faced by most stretcher bearers.

Page 16

(1) **Topic focus:** The problems faced by stretcher bearers on the Western Front.

(2) A shell exploded ahead of his party. One of the bearers was wounded.

(3) Student's own response, but it might resemble the following: Source B is useful as it tells us about the problems faced by stretcher bearers, because it says that a shell exploded ahead of Horton's party. This is useful because it suggests that stretcher bearers worked in dangerous conditions, risking their lives.

(4) Student's own response, as they are all correct, but if you chose the inference made in the answer for **(3)**, you might tick 'Stretcher bearers would carry the wounded from the battlefield at both day and night time.'

(5) Student's own response, but you might write: This is an accurate suggestion, because I know that stretcher bearers would carry casualties from the battlefield at both day and night time, putting them at constant risk from attack.

Page 17

(1) **Nature:** Recollection

Origin: Charles Horton, RAMC stretcher bearer, Third Battle of Ypres, written in 1970

Purpose: Unclear

(2) Student's own response, but you might write:

A It was written as a recollection of the events of Passchendaele.

B Stretcher bearers worked in no man's land to collect the wounded and transport them along the chain of evacuation.

C/D Passchendaele was a bloody battle with over 245,000 British casualties.

E To recollect the events of his job as a stretcher bearer.

(3) Student's own response, but you might write: Source B gives an authoritative view because Horton was a stretcher bearer, who would have worked on the battlefield.

Page 18

(1) Source B is useful for an enquiry about the problems faced by stretcher bearers, because it describes the wound caused by a shell. The stretcher bearer in the source had a shell dressing, **(F)** which suggests that this was a problem that stretcher bearers had to deal with often. This is accurate, as shelling and shrapnel accounted for 58% of the wounds in the First World War. **(A)**

Source B's usefulness is strengthened by the fact it comes from a RAMC stretcher bearer. More authority can be given to the problems described in this source, because the RAMC organised the chain of evacuation. **(D)** This included the difficult transfer from the Regimental Aid Post to the Dressing Station, like the one Horton had to do under fire. **(C)** But this may not be typical as it is only one man's experience. **(E)**

(2) B – The student could have used contextual knowledge, like a description of the poor conditions at Passchendaele, to explain that the problems might have been specific to this battle.

Page 19

(1) Student's own response, but you might write:

What is the topic focus of the enquiry? The problems faced by stretcher bearers.

What can you learn from the content of the source? Stretcher bearers had to work in very muddy conditions, transporting casualties.

What do you know that supports or challenges the accuracy of the contents? Heavy shell bombardments, combined with poor weather, made battlefields like the one at the Third Battle of Ypres very difficult to walk on.

What does the source tell you about its provenance? Nature: Photograph; Origin: British troops, the Third Battle of Ypres, August 1917.

What do you know about the provenance from your contextual knowledge? The British made significant gains during the battle, but the poor weather conditions led to a huge number of British casualties.

How does this affect the strength of the source for the enquiry (refer to criteria)? It makes it less typical of the problems faced by stretcher bearers, as this was a particularly muddy battle.

(2) Student's own response.

Unit 3

Page 22

(1) Student's own response, but you might write:

Generic type of source	Specific type of source
Diary	Diary of a medical officer at a Dressing Station
Records	Records of a Casualty Clearing Station
Statistics	Government statistics of the numbers of medical officers at a Dressing Station
Orders	Orders from the British Army on the procedures at a Casualty Clearing Station
Newspaper	A British newspaper article about the work of RAMC at the Somme
Accounts	The accounts of a Base Hospital near the Western Front

(2) A b; B a; C c; D e; E d

Page 23

(1) A c; B e; C d; D b; E a

(2) **Trench foot:** B and D.

Trench fever: A and E.

Shell shock: C and F.

(3) **a** B

b B

Page 24

(4) **a** A

b C

c C

(5) Regimental Aid Post: 1; Dressing Station: 2; Casualty Clearing Station: 3; Base Hospital: 4; Returned to Britain: 5

(6) Responses should be similar to the words provided below.

chain; medical; front; makeshift; stretcher; Ambulance; walking; Clearing

Page 25

(1) **Highlight:** The effectiveness of the system of transport for the wounded.

(2) Student's own response, but you might write the annotations below.

- There are a lot of medical orderlies or officers to move them.
- Two motor ambulance wagons are available to transport them.
- The wounded are waiting on stretchers.
- The wounded have survived the journey to the Dressing Station from the frontline in the distance.

(3) Student's own response.

(4) **a** Student's own response, but you might write:

Chosen detail	How it relates to the topic
Two motor ambulances are available to transport the wounded.	It relates to how prepared the army were to transport casualties.

b An ambulance driver might have written about workload.

Page 26

(1) (a) The topic focus is the effectiveness of the system of transport for the wounded.

(b) There are three possible correct answers in the table, but you only need to choose one. You could use: There are two motor ambulances. The motor ambulances have covered wagons. Patients are kept on stretchers.

(2) Possible questions depend on which detail is chosen in (1). See ideas below.

Detail in Source A that I would follow up	Question I would ask
There are two motor ambulances.	How common were motor ambulances on the Western Front?
The motor ambulances have covered wagons.	What were the effects of a covered motorised ambulance wagon on the transportation process for the wounded?
Patients are kept on stretchers.	How long did patients have to wait on stretchers at Dressing Stations?

(3) Student's own response.

(4) Student's own response, but you might write:

Detail in Source A that I would follow up: Four men are treating a wounded patient.

Question I would ask: How well trained were the men who provided medical treatment at the Dressing Station?

Page 27

(1) Student's own response, but you might write:

- diaries from casualties who survived the experience
- interviews from medical officers posted at Dressing Stations
- official instructions given to medical staff
- letters from motorised ambulance wagon drivers.

(2) Student's own response.

(3) Student's own response, but you might write:

- Official instructions given to medical staff: might give more details about how long they were supposed to wait before beginning transportation.
- Diaries from casualties: could confirm the impression the detail gives that casualties had to wait quite a long time for transportation, as they are not already on the motorised ambulance wagon.

Page 28

(1) **Tick:** Has the student chosen a detail that relates to the topic in the question?

(2) How many people suffered from frostbite?

(3) Student's own response, but you might write:

- Hospital records from hospitals in Britain.
- Hospital records made by nurses in military hospitals.

- Hospital records of the types of conditions treated in British hospitals during the First World War.

Page 29

(1) Student's own response, but you might write:

1 What is the topic in the question?	The problems of ill health arising from the trench environment.
2 List two to three details in the source that relate to the topic. 3 Highlight one detail that could lead to an enquiry about the topic and that there are likely to be other sources about.	The effects of trench foot or frostbite 'were so bad that they had to be sent back to England'. They had a 'tremendous number of frostbite cases'. 'Their feet were absolutely white, swollen up and dead.'
4 Frame a question that relates to your selected detail, is about an aspect of the topic in the exam-style question and that a historian could answer.	How common was the problem of frostbite on the Western Front?
5 Choose a specific type of source that could provide more details to answer your planned question, place your selected detail in context or could confirm the accuracy of the supplied source.	Records of the RAMC on the number of patients with frostbite sent back to England for treatment in comparison to other conditions.
6 Tick which of these your chosen type of source helps with.	It provides more details to answer your planned question.	
	It places your selected detail in context.	✓
	It confirms that the detail you have selected gives an accurate impression of the situation.	

(2) Student's own response, but you might write:

Detail in Source B that I would follow up: 'We had a tremendous number of frostbite cases at the beginning of 1917.'

Question I would ask: How common was the problem of frostbite on the Western Front?

What type of source I could use: Records of the RAMC on the number of patients with frostbite sent for treatment in comparison to other conditions.

How this might help answer my question: It might reveal whether the problem of frostbite described in Dearnley Military Hospital was a significant problem on the Western Front, or whether it was just that patients with frostbite were sent to that particular hospital in 1917.

Unit 4

Page 32

(1) Describes: A

Explains: B

(2) but

(3) Student's own response, but you might make the following rewrites:

A Disease was prevented by driving off miasma by leaving rubbish on the street in medieval times. ~~It was prevented~~ This practice continued by burning barrels of tar during cholera epidemics in the 19th century.

B Hospitals provided care for the ill in medieval times. ~~They provided~~ and surgical treatment for them in the 19th century.

C People thought an imbalance of the Four Humours caused disease in medieval times ~~and~~. However, Thomas Sydenham argued in the 17th century that it was caused by external factors.

D People believed that God had sent the Black Death. ~~They believed he sent~~ and still believed it during the Great Plague

E Victims of certain diseases were quarantined. Lepers were isolated in lazar houses in medieval times and this practice remained with smallpox sufferers in poxhouses during the 17th century.

F Physicians attempted to cure disease using effective metal cures in the 17th century, ~~and antibiotic cures~~ but they were able to use antibiotics in the 20th century.

Page 33

(1) **1348:** Black Death sufferers are weakened by the use of bloodletting by surgeons.

1500: England has about 1,100 hospitals, but most offer no surgical treatment.

1673: Universities begin to teach William Harvey's ideas about the circulation of blood.

1847: James Simpson discovers chloroform is an effective anaesthetic.

1865: Joseph Lister experiments during surgery with the use of carbolic acid as an antiseptic.

1948: The NHS is set up, giving people access to advanced surgical treatments.

1956: Microsurgery allows the first successful kidney transplants to be performed.

Page 34

(2) A c; B d; C a; D b

(3) **16th and 17th centuries:** C, D, G

19th century: A, E, H

20th and 21st centuries: B, F, I

(4) a Quarantine — To separate people with an infectious disease from the general population.

b Searcher — A person who looked for plague sufferers.

c Vaccination — A mild or alternative form of a disease, helping to prevent a patient from developing a severe form of it.

d Laissez-faire — An attitude that the government should not interfere in the conditions in which people lived.

e Lifestyle campaign — Adverts to change the way people live their lives.

Page 35

(1) a explain

b difference

(2) **Number of features:** one

Number of marks: four

(3) a **Topic focus:** surgical treatment in Britain

b **Timeframes:** 13th and 19th centuries

(4) The stronger student is Student A because they focus on surgical treatment, give detail from the correct timeframes and offer an explanation.

Page 36

(1)

Concept (circle):	Difference
Topic:	Surgical treatment in Britain
Timeframe 1:	13th century
Timeframe 2:	19th century

(2) **Tick:** success rates, risk of infection

Additional areas could include: cost of treatment, level of pain experienced, quality of surgeon

(3) and (4) Student's own response, depending on the answer chosen from (2), but you might write:

Choice: Success rates

13th-century detail: Barber surgeons were poorly qualified to perform surgery.

19th-century detail: Trained surgeons could perform operations quickly, reducing the rate of blood loss.

(4) Student's own response, but you might write: Surgical treatments were performed in a hospital by a professional surgeon.

Page 37

(1), (2) and (3) Student's own response, but you might write:

One way in which surgical treatment in Britain was different was the technology that was used.

In the 13th century, barber surgeons used knives and other barbering equipment.

In the 20th century, surgeons could perform laparoscopic surgery.

This shows that the technology used was more advanced, giving patients a better chance of survival.

Page 38

(1) **Student 1 (strong):** One similarity between the 17th and 19th centuries was what the government tried to prevent (A). In the 17th century, local government officials burned bonfires in the streets to mask bad smells and purify

the air during the Great Plague (B). In the 19th century, they still burned barrels of tar during cholera epidemics (C). This shows that the government was still trying to prevent miasma in the 19th century (D).

(2) **Student 2 (weak):** One similarity between the 17th and 19th centuries was what the government believed about disease (A). In the medieval period, miasma was a popular theory that suggested bad smells caused disease (B). In the 17th century, the government still believed in miasma (C). They were worried that dogs, cats, litter and sewage made the problem worse (D). In the 19th century, the General Board of Health believed cholera was caused by miasma (C). They rejected John Snow's work, which suggested it was to do with the water supply. The board used evidence from the water to try and disprove his work (D). The beliefs stayed the same, because miasma was such a powerful idea (E).

Page 39

(1) Student's own response, but you might write:

Concept (circle):	Difference
Topic:	Government's approaches to the prevention of disease
Timeframe 1:	17th century
Timeframe 2:	19th century

(2) Student's own response, but you might write:

One way in which the government approach to the prevention of disease was different was the level of involvement they had in people's lives.

In the 17th century, Charles II issued decrees to quarantine plague sufferers.

In the 19th century, the government made vaccination against smallpox compulsory.

This shows that the government no longer just tried to stop the spread of disease, but also tried to stop people developing the disease in the first place.

Unit 5

Page 42

(1) A b; B e; C d; D f; E g; F c; G a

(2) Student's own responses, but they might include:

A date: 1852, 1837 and 1840, and 1871

An individual or group: Royal Society, Church and public vaccinators

A named development: Law making vaccination compulsory

A statistic: 35,000 deaths

(3) Student's own response, but it might include:

One reason government involvement changed quickly was that there were now actions the government could take to stop disease. There had been ~~some serious epidemics in the 19th century. Some~~ (1) could have been prevented by ~~new vaccinations~~ (2). This led to rapid change because the government could give its support to vaccination programmes. (3)

(1) 'a smallpox epidemic, killing 35,000 people, between 1837 and 1840. The epidemic'

(2) 'the vaccination developed by Edward Jenner.'

(3) 'as it did in 1871 by appointing public vaccinators.'

Page 43

(1) A a; B b; C b; D a.

(2) The changes were gradual, because people were resistant to change, especially if it meant they had to take action, such as cleaning up the water supply or changing their lifestyle.

(3)
  a False. The ability to measure blood pressure was developed in the 19th century.

  b False. CT scans use advanced x-rays and ultrasound scans use sound.

  c True.

  d False. Penicillin was the first true antibiotic.

  e True.

  f False. Hypodermic needles and insulin pumps are 20th century inventions.

Page 44

(4) a P; b T; c T; d P; e T; f T; g P; h T; i P; j P

(5) 1: E; 2: J; 3: D; 4: C; 5: H; 6: F; 7: B; 8: A; 9: G; 10: I

Page 45

(1) **Underline:** quality of hospital care

  Circle: c1900 to the present day

(2) Student's own response, but you might suggest:

  Institutions: The NHS

  Technology: New diagnosis technology or high-tech medical treatments

  Science: Advances in medicine

(3) Specific information:

  • **New diagnosis technology:** blood tests (1930s), blood sugar monitors (1960s), MRI and CT scans (1970s), ultrasound scans (1940s) and endoscopes (1900s)

  • **High-tech medical treatments:** radiotherapy, dialysis, heart bypass, prosthetic limbs, microsurgery (first kidney transplant in 1956), laparoscopic surgery and robotic surgery

  • **Advances in medicine:**

    o **Magic bullets:** Salvarsan 606 by Hata (1909), Prontosil by Domagk (1932) and M&B 693 by British scientists (1938)

    o **Antibiotics:** Florey and Chain made penicillin into a usable treatment (1940)

    o **Changes in delivery of drugs:** mass production of pills, capsules, hypodermic needles and insulin pumps

    o **Treatment of lung cancer:** transplants, radiotherapy, chemotherapy and pharmacogenomics

(4) Student's own response.

Page 46

(1) Student's own response, but to get a good spread you might choose:

Technology: A

Institutions: E

Science: C

(2) (a) Underline 'why';

(b) tick that they are being asked to explain why a change occurred.

(3) Circle Answer 3.

(4) Student's own response, but you might write:

A – This helped hospitals to perform more successful operations.

E – This meant hospital care was regulated.

Page 47

(1) Underline: quality of hospital care

Circle: c1900 to the present day

(2) and (3) Student's own response, but you might write:

Individuals: Work of Florey and Chain

Institutions: The NHS

Science: Advances in medicines

Technology: High-tech treatments

Attitudes in society: Expectations of hospital care

(4) Student's own response, but you might add:

Left column: Work of Florey and Chain

Right column: Individual scientists provided new drugs for hospitals to use.

(5) This is personal choice, but you might suggest:

Cause (Point): Hospitals were able to provide more effective treatments.

Information (Evidence): Hospitals performed microsurgery, keyhole surgery and robotic surgery.

Cause (Point): Individuals scientists provided new drugs for hospitals to use.

Information (Evidence): Florey and Chain made penicillin into a usable treatment in 1940.

Page 48

(1) (a) and (b)

Strong student answer:

Underline: 1853–54, there was an epidemic that led to over 20,000 deaths; an investigation by John Snow; the passing of the Public Health Act in 1875

Double underline: this led to; because the epidemic created pressure on the government to force local councils to clean up the water supply

Weak student answer:

Underline: several outbreaks of cholera in the 19th century; either due to miasma or a problem with the water supply

Double underline: shows that there were more serious disease problems; led the government's role in the prevention of disease to change quickly

(c) Student A's answer is stronger because it contains precise information with details relating to the question and it remains focused on the concept in the question.

Page 49

(1) (a) Student's own response, but they might write:

Individuals: The work of John Snow

Science: The development of germ theory

Attitudes in society: Smallpox epidemic

(b) and (c) Student's own response, but they might write the following:

The work of John Snow: John Snow presented his findings about the link between water and cholera to Parliament in 1855.

The development of germ theory: Louis Pasteur began work on germ theory in 1861, publishing his work in 1878.

Smallpox epidemic: There was a major smallpox epidemic in 1837–40, killing 35,000 people.

(d) Question concept: Why there was rapid/quick change.

Student's own response to confirm the three pieces of specific information are focused on the question concept.

(2) Student's own response, but they might write:

Cause (Point): John Snow convinced the government to take action.

Information (Evidence): John Snow presented his findings about the link between water and cholera to Parliament in 1855.

Cause (Point): Ideas about the causes of disease made it clear that preventative action could work.

Information (Evidence): Louis Pasteur began work on germ theory in 1861, publishing his work in 1878.

Cause (Point): Fear of smallpox placed pressure on the government to act.

Information (Evidence): There was a major smallpox epidemic in 1837–40, killing 35,000 people.

Unit 6

Page 52

(1) A c; B d; C a; D b

(2) A: (b); B: (c); C: (a); D: (d); E: (e)

Page 53

(1) A: cause; B: prevention; C: cause; D: treatment; E: cause; F: prevention; G: treatment; H: prevention; I: treatment; J: cause; K: treatment; L: prevention

(2) A c; B a; C b; D d

Page 54

(3) Answers in order: classical, Latin, soul, monasteries, conservative, criticised

(4) A: Physician; B: Apothecary; C: Barber surgeon; D: Surgeon; E: Woman

(5) (a) true; (b) false; (c) true; (d) false; (e) false

Page 55

(1) **Underline:** treatment of disease

Circle: changed slowly

(2) Student's own response but you might write:

B Medieval people used humoural treatments.

C Treatment was provided by physicians, who were traditionally trained.

(3) (Based on suggested answers in (2)):

(b) Explain why there was slow change in the use of humoural treatments by medieval people.

(c) Explain why there was slow change in the methods used by physicians.

(4) Student's own response, but based on the questions suggested above you might write:

(b) Books and learning were controlled by the Church.

(c) Medical training was theoretical rather than practical and was based on learning from ancient texts.

(5) Few medieval medical practitioners were trained professionally.

Page 56

(1) Student's own response, but you might write: Sickness was seen as 'proof of the divine'.

(2) **Highlight:** The theories they were trained in

(3) The Church influenced people's views on disease and illness. The Church's view was that sickness was 'proof of the divine'.

(4) One reason treatment changed slowly was that <u>books and learning were controlled by the Church.</u> (Many physicians were clergymen, who trained at universities like Oxford and Cambridge where the study of theology was important.) <u>This meant they followed Church ideas, like using the Four Humours, as part of their treatment plan.</u>

(5) Student's own response.

Page 57

(1) (a) **Topic and concept focus:** 'slow change in the treatment of disease and illness.'

(b) **Reason:** 'traditional approaches were valued.'

(c) **Own knowledge:** 'Physicians used astrology to help diagnose patients and star charts to prescribe treatment.'

(d) **Explanation:** 'This was popular because people believed that the alignment of the stars affected their lives.'

(2) **Link:** 'This led to slow change in treatment, because people would only accept treatments that agreed with their own ideas about how the universe worked.'

(3) Student's own response, but you might write: It led to slow change, because until the Church changed their ideas about treatment, the ideas of physicians would remain the same too.

(4) Student's own response, but you might write: ... a powerful institution promoted them.

Page 58

(1) Point – yellow; Knowledge – Blue; Explanation – Pink; Link back to the question – Green.

(2) **Tick:** Universities relied on books copied by monks.

(3) **Highlight:** It helps to build up your overall argument.

Page 59

(1) Student's own response but you could include the following:

Point: One reason why approaches changed slowly was that the Church was a very influential institution.

Supporting knowledge: Its influence allowed it to spread ideas it liked. For example, the Church liked Galen's idea about humoural treatments.

Explanation: As a result, medical practitioners clung on to old ideas, because they reflected to Church teaching.

Link back to the question: The effect of this was slow change, because it encouraged the continued use of treatments related to the Four Humours.

(2) and (3) Student's own responses.

Unit 7

Page 62

(1) **Tick:** To open a paragraph, focusing on one aspect of the question; To support or illustrate your point with precisely selected information; To explain how your information proves the point you are making; To build up your overall argument in relation to the question set.

(2) (a) **Point:** The change in the way ideas about medicine spread was on an international scale.

(b) **Evidence:** The printing press was developed in Germany around 1440. By 1500, there were hundreds of presses throughout Europe.

(c) **Explanation:** This meant that many more physicians could have direct access to printed texts and the printing press enabled Vesalius' 'Fabric of the Human Body' to be widely distributed in the 16th century.

(d) **Link:** This was a huge change because medical students and professionals across Europe had a new way to learn ideas about medicine and new ideas could be spread more widely and more quickly.

(3) The student's answer should be labeled to identify the following:

(a) **Pace of change:** 1440. By 1500

(b) **Trend:** the way ideas about medicine spread

(c) **Measurements of extent of change:** an international scale; hundreds of presses; huge change

(d) **Direction of change:** a new way to learn about medicine and new ideas could be spread more widely and more quickly

Page 63

(1) a i; b i; c ii; d iii; e iii

(2) (a) could perform operations with a greater understanding of the human body.

(b) it was not taught to students or used in operations.

(c) began to study diseases rather than the nature of patients.

(d) looking to God to explain illness and plan treatments.

Page 64

(2) A d; B a; C c; D b

(3)
a Henry VIII closed down ~~alehouses~~.
Henry VIII closed down bathhouses.

b Homeowners were ~~executed~~ if their street was dirty.
Homeowners were fined if their street was dirty.

c Searchers quarantined victims of ~~syphilis~~.
Searchers quarantined victims of plague.

d The ~~diphtheria~~ vaccination was made compulsory.
The smallpox vaccination was made compulsory.

e Bazalgette built a new sewer system in ~~Birmingham~~.
Bazalgette built a new sewer system in London.

f The Public Health Act (1875) improved water supplies and ~~air~~ and housing quality.
The Public Health Act (1875) improved water supplies and food and housing quality.

(4)
a To stop the spread of syphilis.
b To remove the sources of miasma.
c To prevent the spread of the plague.
d To stop people developing smallpox.
e To limit waterborne bacteria infecting people with cholera.
f To help improve people's health.

Page 65

(1) **Underline:** the spread of ideas about medicine
Highlight: c1400 to c1700

(2) At the start of the period, ideas about medicine spread slowly by word of mouth, through books approved by the Church and through universities controlled by the Church.
At the end of the period, ideas about medicine spread faster through research groups, using pamphlets and books reproduced by the printing press and through universities with greater independence.

(3) Student's own response, but might include:
- The rise in humanism
- The Dissolution of the Monasteries, c1536
- Dissections became more commonplace
- Vesalius' *On the Fabric of the Human Body*, 1543
- The founding of the Royal Society, 1662
- Publication of *Philosophical Transactions*, 1665
- William Harvey's ideas are taught at university, c1673

(4) Student's own response, but might include:
- Charles II grants the Charter founding the Royal Society in 1662
- The declining role of the Church
- Quarantine measures are enforced during the Great Plague, 1665
- The Enlightenment
- Jenner's vaccination, c1796
- Compulsory smallpox vaccinations, 1852
- The Public Health Acts of 1848 and 1875
- News sewers are built in London, c1860

Page 66

(1) **Underline:** the spread of ideas about medicine
Highlight: c1400–c1700
Circle: The invention of the printing press

(2) **a** Books were copied commercially; **b** The spread of information sped up; **c** The Church had less control over book production.

(3) Student's own response, but might include:

Did it affect the pace of change?	
Evidence that the pace of change sped up	Evidence that the pace of change slowed down or stayed the same
Increased the speed of change, as books could be produced at a faster rate.	The Church still controlled universities, limiting the use of books containing ideas they disagreed with.
Did it break with a trend?	
Evidence that it was a major disruption in a trend	Evidence that it was part of a trend of similar changes (list other events/ developments that affected the topic in the question)
It was a major disruption with the way ideas spread, as it was taken out of Church control.	It was part of a trend in: • the declining power of the Church to slow down the speed of ideas, such as the Dissolution of the Monasteries and the development of humanism. • new ways to spread ideas, like the increased use of fugitive sheets. • new ways to develop ideas, like the foundation of the Royal Society.
Did it affect the direction of change?	
Evidence that it led to progress (things improved)	Evidence that it did not lead to progress or that things stayed the same/grew worse
It led to progress in the range of ideas spread.	It took a while for new ideas to develop that could be spread, such as Vesalius' work challenging Galen in 1543.

(4) Student's own response but might include: An argument that the printing press was a turning point was that it also helped advances in the range of ideas spread. However, it may not have been a turning point as the pace of change was still slowed by the Church.

Page 67

(4) **Underline:** the way ideas about medicine spread.
Highlight: c1400–c1700

(2)

State of affairs c1400	State of affairs c1700
Ideas spread through books produced by monks in monasteries.	Ideas spread through books produced by printing presses.
Universities spread ideas that were promoted by the Church.	New universities were influenced by humanism.
Popular ideas about medicine spread by word of mouth.	Popular ideas about medicine spread by word of mouth.

③	What was the scale of the change?	International
	In the areas of attitudes of people, power of institutions and scientific knowledge, what was the level of progress?	Significant progress
	How much continuity was there between the start and end of the period?	Suggested mark: 3 (word of mouth was still used to spread popular ideas among ordinary people)

④ **a** The scale of change during this period was international, as the printing press became the main way in which books were produced and ideas spread in Europe.

b During the period there was significant progress, as universities had more control over the spread of ideas, while the Church's hold was weakened.

c Overall, there was some continuity between the start and end of the period.

Page 68

① The student answer should be annotated as below:

- Changes they have used as evidence
- Criteria for evaluating a turning point
- References to extent of change

The printing press sped up the spread of ideas. Before the printing press, books were produced by monks who wrote them out by hand. After the printing press was developed by Gutenberg in 1440, books could be copied by machine. For example, lots of copies were made of Vesalius' book 'On the Fabric of the Human Body'. This process was faster because machine production could outpace production by hand. This made the printing press a turning point, because new ideas could spread quickly across Europe, as lots of copies of new books like Vesalius' could be produced and distributed in a short space of time.

However, the printing press was also part of a trend of similar changes in the spread of ideas. In the 16th century, the ideas of humanism became more influential, which encouraged a break with medieval ideas. This continued into the 17th century, when the Royal Society was set up to discuss new scientific ideas. Both of these developments meant ideas could spread because people were more willing to accept and discuss them. This suggests the printing was less of a turning point, because it was a part of a trend towards sharing ideas.

② Students should tick all three rows of the checklist.

Page 69

① Student's own response, but might include:

- The use of quarantine broke with a general government approach of lack of involvement in everyday life.
- On the other hand, it did not speed up the pace of change, because quarantine was only a short-term measure.
- It was also part of similar changes, like the ban on bathhouses, which was not disrupted until the government had a new means to prevent disease.

- A far more significant turning point can be seen in government legislation in the mid-19th century to enforce vaccination and public health works in towns.

② Student's own response, but a suggested answer would be:

The actions taken to prevent the spread of plague were part of similar changes in the previous century and the trend was not disrupted until the 19th century. For example, the government had already tried to stop the spread of disease in the 16th century when Henry VIII closed down bathhouses. It was not until the smallpox vaccination was developed in the late 18th century that there was a turning point in the role of the government. This suggests the trend was not disrupted until the government had an effective way to support the prevention of disease. This means that the Great Plague was not a turning point, but just part of a trend towards greater government involvement.

Unit 8

Page 72

① **a** B; **b** A; **c** C; **d** C

② Students should tick the first student answer.

Page 73

① **1880s:** An instrument for measuring blood pressure is first used.

1890s: X-rays are used to find broken bones and aid surgeons.

1900s: Endoscopes are used to take pictures of the inside of the human body.

1931: Ernst Ruska and Max Knoll develop the electron microscope.

1930s: Bloods tests are used for diagnosis of a wide range of illnesses and disease.

1940s: Ultrasound scans are used to look for kidney stones and gall stones.

1948: The NHS is set up, providing greater access to new methods of diagnosis.

Page 74

② A g; B f; C e; D b; E d; F c; G a

③ AV: A, D, E.

WH: B, C, F.

④ **Answers in order:** Church, dissection, fugitive, humanism, religion, Sydenham

Page 75

① **Underline:** the diagnosis of illness and disease

Circle: the 19th and 20th centuries

Highlight: technology was the most important factor

② and ③ Student's own response, but might include:

- Individuals: N/A
- Institutions: The role of the government X
- Science: New ideas about the cause of disease X

- Technology: Technology used by research scientists ✓
- Attitudes in society: N/A

④ Student's own response, but you might include:

- Research technology: Technology helped develop ideas that could be used in diagnosis.
- Ideas about the cause of disease: New ideas about illness and disease made diagnosis possible.
- The government: Institutions and organisations gave funding to research and providing diagnosis.

⑤ Student's own response.

Page 76

① Student's own response, but you might write: Was it the work of individuals on the cause of disease or the attitudes of society towards what caused disease that improved diagnosis?

② and ③ Student's own response might include:

Point	It was **technology** that led to improved diagnosis.	It was the work of the **individual** who used technology that improved diagnosis.
Evidence	The development of the electron microscope in 1931.	The work of Francis and Crick on the science of genetics.
Explanation	The electron microscope made it possible to view DNA more closely, diagnosing genetic diseases.	Francis and Crick's work allowed DNA to be mapped in order to diagnose genetic diseases.
Weight		+

④ Student's own response, but you might write: Technology is only significant when individuals help realise its potential.

Page 77

① Student's own response, but you might add the following additional arguments:

- **For:** Technology improved the range of diagnoses that were possible.
- **Against:** Scientists came up with the ideas needed to make a diagnosis.

② Student's own response, but you might weight as follows:

A For: Technology enabled discoveries to be made that were crucial for improvements in diagnosis. +3

B For: Technology improved the range of diagnoses that were possible. +5

C Against: Institutions provided patients with access to diagnostic equipment. −2

D Against: Scientists came up with the ideas needed to make a diagnosis. −3

③ Student's own response, but you might write:

B: It made possible a huge range of diagnoses.

C: It was only important towards the end of the period and depended on the other causes to have an impact.

D: Their ideas led to accurate diagnoses for many people, but their discovery depended on the technology.

Page 78

① Suggested annotations are as follows:

Strong student response:

A: without their ideas; and helped so many people; doctors needed ideas about disease that were advanced enough; slowed improvements; only temporary; helping them make discoveries; to exploit the technology

B: was more important than the work of the government, because even though; relied on improvements in

C: work of scientists; the founding of the NHS in 1948; individuals; technology; without individual scientists

Weak student response:

D: because they were important to improvements in diagnosis; by scientists who were important

E: there were other reasons like the work of the government and advances in technology

F: blood tests were introduced in the 1930s, making diagnosis easier

Page 79

① and ③ Student's own response, but you might include:

Point 1: Vesalius challenged a number of ideas about the human body. (+5)

Point 2: His work influenced medical students. (+4)

Point 3: The declining power of the Church helped the study of the human body. (−3)

Point 4: A change in attitude led to greater experimentation and questioning of old ideas about the human body. (−2)

② Referring to the suggestions above, you might highlight that points 1 and 3 conflict. Point 1 made the bigger contribution, because for developments to be made, there needed to be someone who could take advantage of the declining power of the Church, like Vesalius.

④ Student's own response, but an appropriate answer might be:

The work of Vesalius was the main reason for developments in the understanding of the human body, because his ideas were influential throughout the 16th and 17th centuries. They also influenced many students, affecting the understanding of the body for future generations of medical practitioners. However, this was made possible by the declining power of the Church and the rising influence of humanism, allowing old ideas to be questioned and investigated. Nevertheless, without people like Vesalius to take advantage of this situation, little would have changed.

Notes